ENGINEERS:
THE ANATOMY OF A PROFESSION

WITHDRAWN

Engineers:
The Anatomy of a Profession

A STUDY OF MECHANICAL ENGINEERS IN BRITAIN

J. E. GERSTL & S. P. HUTTON

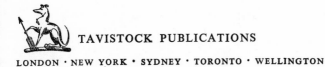
TAVISTOCK PUBLICATIONS

LONDON · NEW YORK · SYDNEY · TORONTO · WELLINGTON

First published in 1966
by Tavistock Publications Limited
11 New Fetter Lane London EC4
Printed in Great Britain
in 10 pt Times New Roman, 2 pt leaded
by Butler and Tanner Ltd, Frome and London

Contents

Tables

Figures

Foreword

The importance of engineers in our technological age hardly needs to be documented, but their position in modern society cannot be fully appreciated without attention to the structure and dynamics of their profession. Our study of the anatomy of the engineering profession aims to provide this information. It is based upon a survey of mechanical engineers in Britain conducted in 1962.

The circumstances that gave rise to our work in this area were to a certain extent fortuitous, representing the combined professional concerns of an engineer and an occupational sociologist arriving on the staff of University College, Cardiff, about the same time. Hutton had recently been appointed the first Professor of Mechanical Engineering at Cardiff, and Gerstl had come from America for two years as Lecturer in Industrial Sociology in the Industrial Relations Department. The inauguration of a separate Mechanical Engineering Department at the university provided a good opportunity for rethinking some issues of educational policy. Given the limited period of a three-year engineering course, it was essential to design a syllabus that would be of the utmost benefit to the student, bearing in mind his occupational role and the country's future needs. It was not certain that to follow the traditional pattern of education would necessarily be the best policy.

In order to determine the essential educational requirements of future mechanical engineers it is necessary to know precisely what a mechanical engineer is and what are the main types of work he will be expected to do at various stages of his career. In seeking to answer these basic questions in relation to a particular profession it became apparent that a number of more general issues were involved on which there had been little previous investigation to serve as guidelines. The present volume reports our findings.

The authors gratefully acknowledge the help afforded by many individuals and organizations. The Department of Scientific and Industrial Research financed the investigation and provided guidance. Invaluable assistance in all phases of the work was given by Social Surveys (Gallup Poll) Ltd, whose staff helped in designing and pretesting the questionnaire, in selecting the sample and carrying out the interviews, and in coding, card-punching, and tabulating the data; we especially wish to thank Dr H. Durant, Miss Leslie Austen, and Mrs Naomi MacIntosh for their contributions. The Institution of Mechanical Engineers and the Engineers' Guild gave us the benefit of their experience. We are indebted to Professor Michael Fogarty and Colonel Work for their enthusiasm and constructive suggestions in the early stages of the study, and to Professor David Glass for his comments on the questionnaire. Mrs Jill Briggs did much of the typing in the later stages with sustained cheerfulness. We also thank the many interested people whom we consulted beforehand, and finally the many busy engineers who kindly took part in the survey.

CHAPTER 1

Engineering as a profession

THE EVOLUTION OF THE ENGINEER

Although engineering is often regarded as a relatively new field, a product of the industrial revolution, its roots were laid in antiquity. Irrigation, mining, and metal-working, for example, go back thousands of years.

Each era has had its particular problems, which have had to be solved by the wisdom, experience, and skills available at the time. Over the centuries the engineer has evolved from the simple craftsman who, as he was called upon to make larger and more complicated devices, developed increasingly refined practical techniques and eventually required all the resources of science to produce the sophisticated engineering designs of today (Hutton, 1962). Throughout the ages the work of the engineer has been closely associated with the life and economy of the community and his skills have been utilized for both military and civil applications. For thousands of years man's life had been essentially agricultural and, even to provide for the more sophisticated life of the cities or to build such wonders as the pyramids, there had been no need for more complicated machines than the wheel and the lever. There were many craftsmen and a few important machines, such as windmills, waterwheels, cranes, and looms, but, generally speaking, man was able to get along using stone, wood, and small amounts of metal in his ingenious but uncomplicated machines. As long as the economy was agricultural and therefore simple, there was little use for engineering on a large scale. However, as the ancient civilizations developed and eventually the industrial revolution swept Europe, craftsmen assumed increasing responsibility, becoming master builders and, later, the great engineers of the nineteenth century. These were the men who flung networks of roads, canals, and railways across Europe and subsequently America; built iron ships and locomotives; developed ingenious machinery for the manufacturing industry and thereby helped to accelerate the industrial revolution which had started in the 'wooden age'.

If any period in history can be singled out as the one in which the engineer as we know him emerged, it is probably the eighteenth century. Initially he was a military engineer, whose skills were required for designing fortresses and solving the intricacies of ordnance. Napoleon, a great patron of the sciences, profoundly influenced engineering by establishing special schools to educate sufficient numbers of military engineers for his needs. These schools have since become the exclusive *grandes écoles* of France which now produce the polytechnicians, the intellectual élite of the country. The modern engineer began life therefore as a military specialist, but because of the social and economic changes of the eighteenth and nineteenth centuries he developed even more rapidly as a civil engineer, and later diversified into the various specialized branches of technology that we know today. The almost insatiable demands of our present rapidly developing technological age, whose wealth is so largely based upon engineering products, now require engineers who not only have the necessary practical experience but also have been educated in mathematics, in the basic engineering sciences, and in related fields. These are the leaders of the engineering industry, the relatively new professional class with whom we are concerned. Because of the enormous range covered by engineering and the peculiarities of its historical development, many special branches have come into being, which together constitute the four main groups: civil, electrical, mechanical, and chemical engineering.

THE ROLE OF ENGINEERING IN A TECHNOLOGICAL AGE

In the extremely complex and changing life of the developing countries that depend on technology for their daily wants, increasing reliance is placed upon professional people of all kinds who, by their education and training, have become expert in some special field. Not only are the old professions such as law and medicine essential, but so are many new ones in the fields of economics, finance, science, technology, and sociology – this last is concerned with the many human problems that arise from our rapid development. As the Duke of Edinburgh has pointed out (1961), if the underdeveloped areas are to progress, a variety of specialists is needed, but it tends to be the engineers and the medicals who are required first, because of their capacity to deal with the basic problems of food, health, water-supply, sanitation, and transport and communications. These are the essential services upon which can be founded sound agriculture, commerce, and industry. Thus all professional people, and particularly engineers, have a creative part to play in the development of both old and new countries. The relation between engineering and the other professions depends very much on the stage of development reached by the particular country concerned. In Britain and many other countries science and technology not only are of social and economic significance; they have also become great political issues upon which governments may rise or fall.

CRITERIA OF PROFESSIONALISM

There can be little question that the professions have a major role in industrial society, and that an essential contribution is made by the scientific and technological professions. There is increasing need for the specialized functions of professional people, who constitute a growing proportion of the labour force. Unfortunately, the very term 'profession' has curiously and significantly managed to evade numerous attempts to establish its confines or even to circumscribe its general domain (see, for example, Carr-Saunders & Wilson, 1933; Parsons, 1939; Lewis & Maude, 1952; Hughes, 1958; Bucher & Strauss, 1961; Kornhauser, 1962; Barber, 1963; Millerson, 1964; and Wilensky, 1964a). Apart from the confusion engendered by loose usage of the term in everyday speech, its continued ambiguity is also due to the transformations that have altered the historical models of the professions, the diverse characteristics of occupations claiming professional status, and the vested interests of many who have attempted to grapple with the concept.

Critical evaluations have, on the one extreme, suggested that the only agreed characteristic of professions is a eulogistic terminology, or even more strongly that 'profession' is not a sociological category (Habenstein, 1963), and, on the other, found that the various commonly cited definitions and criteria indicate a commendable unanimity (Goode, 1960). While it appears that the differences between definitions are more frequently those of emphasis or omission than of contradiction, the unanimity certainly does not extend to agreement as to which are core and which derivative traits of professions.

The core trait about which there seems to be the greatest agreement is that of specialized qualifications, epitomized in the term '*learned* professions'; it is incorporated in dictionary definitions of the word 'profession', and demonstrated organizationally in the founding purpose of qualifying associations. A second basic characteristic of professionalism is also suggested by a verbal clue, '*free* professions'; this signifies independence in the carrying out of the special competence; it does not necessarily imply absence of supervision, but entails freedom for the individuals to profess their esoteric branch of knowledge, and a degree of self-control frequently formalized in a code of ethics. Strong commitment – attachment to intrinsic occupational goals – is a third basic characteristic of professionalism, one which has received less attention than it warrants. Social responsibility and community interest tend to be subsumed by professional commitments, as opposed to work which is regarded merely as a means to an end. Similarly, the reward system of professions, which often values social honour or prestige more highly than income, is intimately bound up with the degree of commitment.

The application of these criteria would indicate that, within any occupational group, some practitioners work in a situation more conducive to professionalism than others. For example, there are often built-in strains between work organizations and professional institutions, to which the engineer is particularly susceptible (see Kornhauser, 1962). Some work settings will facilitate professional interests more readily than others. In our occupational analysis of the professional engineer, the criteria of professionalism provide a basic framework.

THE PROFESSIONAL ENGINEER

Recently EUSEC (the conference of engineering societies of Western Europe and the United States of America) has spent much time in defining the work of the professional engineer in considerable detail:

'A professional engineer is competent by virtue of his fundamental education and training to apply scientific method and outlook to the analysis and solution of engineering problems. He is able to assume personal responsibility for the development and application of engineering science and knowledge, notably in research, designing, construction, manufacturing, superintending, managing, and in the education of the engineer. His work is predominantly intellectual and varied, and not of a routine mental or physical character. It requires the exercise of original thought and judgement and the ability to supervise the technical and administrative work of others.

His education will have been such as to make him capable of closely and continuously following progress in his branch of engineering science by consulting new published work on a worldwide basis, assimilating such information and applying it independently. He is thus placed in a position to make contributions to the development of engineering science or its applications.

His education and training will have been such that he will have acquired a broad and general appreciation of the engineering sciences as well as a thorough insight into the special features of his own branch. In due time he will be able to give authoritative technical advice, and to assume responsibility for the direction of important tasks in his branch' (EUSEC, 1961).

Such a definition is necessary because it is only in a few countries such as Germany that the term engineer is protected by law and that the function of engineers is relatively well understood. In Britain engineer is a particularly vague term, covering anything from a plumber to a Fellow of the Royal Society. In other countries, particularly on the Continent, the term is used with more discrimination and so is more meaningful to the public, and it conjures up an image of somebody much nearer to a professional man than to an artisan.

Engineering differs from most other professions because of its basic creative role in harnessing natural resources to provide economic wealth. During the last hundred years its importance has been greatly enhanced owing to the increasing dependence upon it of the developed countries for supplies of essentials such as fuel and power and basic materials such as steel and plastics, not to mention the many consumer goods that are characteristic of modern life. Clearly, the engineering profession has a vital part to play in world economy.

SCIENCE AND ENGINEERING

Whereas in the nineteenth century the great engineers were public figures and the results of their work were obvious to all in the form of railways, roads, bridges, and steamships, the work of the professional engineer in the twentieth century is masked by the complex technical and economic structure that has grown round him. Not only is engineering inextricably involved with financial and economic matters, but even on the technical level it is closely related to science, to such a degree, in fact, that the press and the public refer to many engineers as scientists, with resulting distortions to the image of both. For example, the wonderful achievements of space research are almost invariably regarded as scientific successes, although they depend very largely upon high-class engineering. There are distinctive differences between science and engineering, which must be appreciated. Science is concerned essentially with knowledge for its own sake and with the search for truth. In contrast, although scientific techniques and the knowledge obtained from scientific research are valuable tools in engineering, its object is quite different. Engineering is concerned with creating devices that will be useful; that will, moreover, in most cases sell at an economic price. The engineer in fact is the medium through which the general public is able to enjoy the fruits of the latest scientific discoveries. Science itself is heavily dependent upon the engineering industry, which manufactures instruments and apparatus to enable physicists, chemists, and the host of other pure scientists to take their investigations further. The translation of modern scientific discoveries into economic wealth is, then, technically in the hands of the engineers and administratively the responsibility of the financiers, who have the job of making new developments an economic proposition. It is mainly in military engineering that the engineer is freed from the task of compromising between technical and economic requirements, because here it is usually a case of meeting performance requirements at any cost. Although, therefore, science and engineering are interdependent, and must remain so, the engineer always approaches his task with a practical objective in mind and with a philosophy different from that of the scientist. His work is more varied than the scientist's, and not only must he be capable of creating new designs, but he will often have the task of putting plans into action, taking people with him and getting the best out of them, and working within an economic framework linked with commerce and finance.

DEVELOPMENT OF ENGINEERING EDUCATION

Relations between science and engineering are similar in a number of countries, but for historical and social reasons the relative status of the two professions varies considerably. Where engineering has a higher status, it is perhaps partly explained by the more rapid and clear-cut development of engineering education in the countries concerned, but social and economic factors also affect this issue. Although Britain's practical contribution to the development of engineering in the nineteenth century was considerable, the Continental countries were far in advance educationally when they established separate technical universities to train professional engineers. Many of the Continental engineering schools were founded in the late eighteenth century under state or royal patronage. Among some of the earliest were St Petersburg (Timoshenko, 1959), Prague, and Berlin. These were nearly all new institutions, independent of existing universities and created to meet the special needs of a growing technology. In contrast, in Britain it was not until the middle of the nineteenth century that anything active was done, and this was to form engineering departments in the new provincial universities which were growing up at that time. The oldest engineering college in Britain is Anderson's College, Glasgow, which was founded in 1797 for artisans. This later became the Royal Technical College and is now the University of Strathclyde, one of the new technological universities. It seems that because engineering departments were part of universities, for social and political reasons they did not grow as rapidly as they should have done; indeed, this is one of the reasons why Colleges of Advanced Technology were instituted in 1957 by the Ministry of Education. On the Continent, however, the Technische Hochschulen and the Écoles Polytechniques, despite their titles, flourished as independent technical universities, and, as a result, their status is higher than that of their British counterparts and the status of the engineering profession is much higher.

In the engineering professions of most countries there is a recognized two-tier structure. The top tier consists of university-trained engineers who, on the Continent, have had a five or six years' course, graduating with the title Diplomingenieur, Ingénieur Diplomé, or, in the Scandinavian countries, Civil Ingenieur. The second tier, separately defined by EUSEC (1961), comprises 'engineering technicians', who have studied for three or four years at a lower academic level, receiving, nevertheless, a thorough technical training at special schools that are not of university status, known in different countries as Ingenieurschulen or Écoles d'Ingénieurs des Arts et Métiers. In Britain there is a similar but not identical structure, in which both tiers are included in the corporate membership of the engineering

B

institutions so that both university graduates and those educated at technical colleges have the same professional qualification awarded by the institution – for example, Associate Member of the Institution of Mechanical Engineers. In America, professional engineers are mostly college graduates but, in practice, they have large numbers of well-trained technicians to help them. Top-grade professional engineers are therefore analogous to commissioned officers in the army, and the next grade to non-commissioned officers. These two groups lead and direct the activities of the many technicians, craftsmen, and unskilled workers who constitute the engineering industry. Naturally, those at the top have to be the initiators, the creators, and the thinkers, but they need a large and highly trained team of people of differing ability and experience to put their plans into action and to convert designs into reality.

In America, the professional engineer must be registered by the state in which he wishes to practise; on the Continent he must have a recognized degree or qualification, which is awarded by the state; and in Britain he must satisfy the qualifying examinations of the various engineering institutions. In Europe, as a result of moves towards a common market and economic unity, there has been considerable collaboration among the engineering societies of the different countries, with a view to establishing common technical and professional standards and reciprocal membership qualifications so that an engineer, once qualified, may be readily employed in any part of Europe. The trend is actually towards registration of professional engineers through the work of FEANI (Fédération Européene d'Associations Nationales d'Ingénieurs; see Engineers' Guild, 1963), a body concerned with general professional matters as opposed to educational and technical qualifications (the province of EUSEC). There is a similar distinction in Britain between the Engineers' Guild (see p. 10 below) and the engineering institutions.

Although there has been some progress towards standardization, differences remain between the engineering professions of various countries. For instance, in Britain the system is comparatively flexible and it is possible for an exceptionally good engineer who has not been university-trained to rise to the top of his profession; in many European countries this is almost impossible. Whereas in Britain engineering students spend three years at university, in almost every other country in the world they must study five or six years before graduating.

The problem of recruiting to the profession adequate numbers of entrants of high calibre is common to all countries; its severity, however, varies considerably according to the local situation as regards the supply of technical manpower to serve the needs of rapidly expanding industry. The extent of the recruitment problem thus depends, in each country, on the prevailing social conditions, on the status of the profession and, most important, on the system of school education. In countries, such as Britain, where engineering has a relatively low status and where there is a shortage of mathematics and science teachers in the schools, recruitment of engineers is particularly difficult. In America also, during the last five years, largely because of the glamour of the space-research programme, there has been a serious decrease in the relative numbers of top-class undergraduates in engineering and a corresponding increase in the numbers in physics and chemistry (*New Society*, 1964).

The problems of one country may not be typical of another, but nevertheless they are likely to be comparable in some broad aspects. Indeed, even contrasts would be instructive. It is surprising, however, how few data are available on the engineering professions in various countries and how little serious research has been done on the important question of training and utilizing engineers. We may look briefly at some of the difficulties confronting the profession in Britain.

ENGINEERING IN BRITAIN TODAY

To be a chartered engineer in Britain one must be a corporate member of one of the chartered engineering institutions which were established during the early part of the nineteenth century. The first of these bodies in Britain was the Institution of Civil Engineers, founded in 1818 by a group of enthusiasts who had previously been meeting regularly in a London coffee house, and who chose as their first president Thomas Telford, an eminent builder of roads, bridges, and harbours. The Institution relied on pupilage under a member as a method of training, and soon assumed the function of a qualifying body in addition to that of a learned society. It is of interest that the Institution of Mechanical Engineers is said to have originated as a splinter group formed by some railway engineers from the north of the country. The incident that is supposed to have triggered off their action is that George Stephenson, a great railway engineer, refused to submit 'a probationary essay as a proof of his capacity as an engineer' when applying to join the Institution of Civil Engineers. Whether or not this is true, Stephenson certainly became the first president of the Institution of Mechanical Engineers when it was founded in 1847. It is more likely, however, that the new body came into being to meet needs deriving from differences between London and the provinces (Millerson, 1964). It has grown to be the largest of the engineering institutions, with a membership of 60,000.

There are now in Britain thirteen major engineering institutions holding royal charters;[1] they include modern specialities such as radio engineering, production engineering, and chemical engineering. Because of a feeling that the existence of so many different institutions is not in the best interests of the profession, these thirteen have recently established the Engineering Institutions Joint Council (EIJC),[2] whose declared object is 'to promote and coordinate in the public interest the development of the science, and the practice and profession of engineering'. A similar function is performed for the medical profession by the General Medical Council, which safeguards academic standards and acts as a qualifying body. The two professions differ, however, in that the medical profession has another body, the British Medical Association, to protect members' interests and look after general professional matters such as salaries and working conditions. In contrast, the charters of the individual engineering institutions and the proposed terms of reference of the EIJC preclude them from doing anything that would be of direct financial benefit to their members. For instance, the charter of 'the mechanicals' states: 'The Institution shall not carry on any trade or business or engage in any transaction with a view to the pecuniary gain or profit of the members thereof.' They can therefore act only as qualifying bodies and learned societies. Because of these limitations of the main institutions, a small but active organization known as the Engineers' Guild[3] was set up in 1937. It is now open to all corporate members of the institutions that are affiliated to the newly created EIJC, and it is concerned with the wider professional issues.

[1] The Royal Aeronautical Society; the Institutions of Civil Engineers; of Electrical Engineers; of Electronic & Radio Engineers; of Gas Engineers; of Marine Engineers; of Mechanical Engineers; of Mining Engineers; of Municipal Engineers; of Production Engineers; of Structural Engineers; the Institute of Mining & Metallurgy; the British Institution of Radio Engineers.

[2] Now by Royal Charter, 1965, the Council of the Engineering Institutions (CEI) (see App. 4).   [3] See App. 4.

Its object, 'to promote and maintain the unity, public usefulness, honour, and interests of the engineering profession', is superficially similar to that of EIJC, but it performs among other things a protective function in terms of employment, pensions, salaries, and status, which affect the individual engineer (Engineers' Guild, 1964a). The membership of the Engineers' Guild is only about 5,500; it is increasing, however, as the inadequacies of the institutions regarding general professional matters are more clearly revealed.

In sum, the engineering profession in Britain suffers from undue diversification, there being so many different professional institutions and qualifications that the public is confused and the profession's image is blurred. The layman cannot be blamed if the technologists are inarticulate; or if they are wrapped up in their work or hindered by the traditional constraints of their professional structure to such an extent that they fail to see the need to gain general recognition for the undoubtedly important services that they provide.

Another problem to be considered is how to achieve efficient utilization of technical labour. Not only have the relative needs of the various professions to be satisfied in the best interests of the national economy, but within engineering the relative numbers of graduate and non-graduate engineers, technicians, and skilled and unskilled workers must be maintained so as to ensure maximum productivity. As we shall see, Britain differs from America and some of the Continental countries in the order of priority given to different types of engineering work function and in the proportions of kinds of labour used. There is evidence to suggest that Britain is not employing its engineers to the best advantage and that many of them are engaged on tasks that do not require their training and capabilities.

Even if engineers and ancillary staff are efficiently employed and are coming forward in sufficient numbers, there still remains the problem of what is the best form of education and training. In the rapidly changing industrial climate of today, it is by no means certain that the very limited time available for formal education is being used in the most appropriate way. It is clear that a small, densely populated country such as Britain must earn its living in the future by means of its skills and the resulting value of the goods it exports. A very high proportion of these essential exports are engineering products: it has been estimated (Hartley, 1964) that the British engineering industry contributes, directly, about 35 per cent and, indirectly, about 60 per cent of the gross national product. Yet despite the industry's vital role in the economic survival of the country through its contribution to the practical task of competing in the world market, the profession's status in Britain is lower than that of several of the older professions. Some of the reasons for this lack of recognition are not hard to find: one is certainly the proliferation of engineering institutions mentioned previously; another can be traced to the attitudes within the universities towards engineering. In the conservative and rarefied atmosphere of the universities, science was a relative newcomer as an academic discipline. It was only natural, therefore, that classics and arts should, until recently, have been regarded as much higher forms of academic life. Similarly with the latecomer, engineering: in the older universities, particularly Oxford, it was looked down upon as something rather ungentlemanly and hardly a fit subject for university study. This attitude persists in public life as a form of snobbism that regards engineering as inferior to science; it can be explained partly in terms of ignorance and partly as a hangover from the nineteenth century. Unfortunately, its effects are still seen in the shortage of high-quality recruits to the engineering profession in Britain. Just as science has to compete with the arts, so engineering has to compete with science, which at the moment has more glamour and respectability (Ashby, 1958).

Britain seems to be at a disadvantage, when compared with other countries, in several other ways. First, it has always lagged behind in terms of the number of university graduates per head of population. For instance, Bowden (1959) pointed out that fifty years ago Britain 'had fewer universities in proportion to our population than any other civilized country in Europe with the exception of Turkey'. The position today is little changed. Out of twenty-eight countries, Britain is twenty-fifth in terms of university students per head of population. The proportion of young people who go to university in Australia is already three times higher than it is in Britain. Second, Britain is experiencing a serious shortage of science, and particularly mathematics, teachers. Moreover, schoolboys do not appear to be attracted towards a career in engineering to the same extent that they are in Canada and Sweden, for example. Hutchings (1963) has suggested that this is partly because the status of the engineering profession is lower in Britain than in most other countries; partly because schoolmasters are usually graduates in arts or, at best, pure science, and are inevitably ignorant of the work of the professional engineer; and partly because of the attraction of pure science and the human appeal of the arts, sociology, and economics. It has been found (Ministry of Education, 1963*a*) that although the proportion of sixth-formers taking science as opposed to arts subjects increased slightly up to 1962, since then the arts have once again begun to draw more students.

The engineering institutions, although aware of the situation, have not until recently been very active in the sphere of public relations with a view to improving the image of engineering by means of films, articles, and talks that the layman could readily appreciate. Perhaps the BBC television programme 'Mechanical Man', shown in July 1964, may be regarded as an encouraging example of the kind of activity that needs to be undertaken. Even so, the image presented holds little of the glamour that attaches to the popular 'Dr Kildare'. Furthermore, a glamorous and prestigeful image will not by itself solve recruitment problems, for the medical profession is also suffering as far as good-quality entrants are concerned.

THE NEED FOR RESEARCH

From the foregoing it is evident that there are many problems facing the engineering profession in Britain today. The basic questions of engineering education and shortage of technical manpower have been widely debated in mainly subjective terms, and many recommendations have been made on a minimum of factual evidence. For instance, although industry bewails its recruitment difficulties and politicians complain about losses through emigration and the 'brain drain', surprisingly little is known about the engineer himself, or his career once his education and training are completed. Similarly, there is much confusion about engineering education, which has developed in haphazard fashion in Britain, after a late start, with the result that current ideas and practices are based largely upon tradition, politics, and prejudice. A more objective and dispassionate approach is obviously necessary if the challenge of our times is to be met. As was stated above, it is by no means certain that professional engineers are being adequately trained or used to the best advantage in industry. The present study is an attempt to redress the balance by providing some facts about one group, mechanical engineers, and their profession, which may serve as a basis for more authoritative discussion in the future, and more mature judgements.

Often in the past too narrow a view has been taken, and it must be emphasized at the outset that issues such as the education, training, and utilization of mechanical engineers can be fruitfully examined only in the context of national needs. For instance, Britain is only just realizing that its future need for technicians may be even more urgent than its demand for engineers, which itself is pressing enough.

It is also necessary, whenever the education of engineers is being discussed, to take into account the pattern of school education in the country concerned, since the two cannot be separated. Under the British structure, for instance, there is some conflict between the desire to offer a wide and liberal education at school to the age of 18 years and the need to comply with entrance requirements to university engineering courses, which include a high standard of attainment in science and engineering subjects. This problem will be overcome only through the closer integration of school and university syllabuses. It arises, of course, in relation to further education in a variety of fields.

The general problems of education and technical manpower need to be tackled on a national basis by some authoritative body having access to reliable factual information on economics, manpower, resources, and all other relevant factors. As C. E. Carter (1963) has pointed out:

'If we do not have an economic policy about the distribution of scientific resources, we are unlikely to have any policy at all . . . A starting point for scientific policy is the examination of what we know about the pattern of exports ten to twenty years ahead . . . At many points there will be a temptation to suppose that the problem of distribution of scientific effort is too difficult, complex and vague to be solved. Yet a few tentative moves towards rationality may be better than leaving the disposal of a valuable resource to random and undirected influences.'

A start in this direction has been made by the National Economic Development Council, and also by such interesting research projects as the economic growth model set up on computers at Cambridge. We nevertheless have a long way to progress. The Robbins Committee (Ministry of Education, 1963a) was one of the first in the field to take a broad view of the problem of education, upon the basis of extensive statistical data that it collected. A similar approach is needed to establish the relative priorities to be given to the various professions and academic disciplines.

A first step is to determine what proportions of unskilled, skilled, and professional people, in all fields, will be required, and whether these can be provided without interfering with the plans for other sections of the economy. Some countries, such as Norway, already make an annual comprehensive survey, on the basis of which educational and other priorities are established. It must be decided how many engineers are required compared with scientists, doctors, economists, sociologists, accountants, and arts graduates. What proportions of engineering graduates, of Honours, Pass Degree, Dip. Tech., Higher National Certificate, and part-time students will be needed, and how many technicians per engineer? Such distributions must be studied if a country is to get any idea of the structure of its future economy, which will in turn influence educational needs.

CHAPTER 2

Scope and method of the investigation

PAUCITY OF STUDIES IN THE FIELD

The crucial importance of the role of the technological professions in industrial societies would appear obvious. On the basis of numerical preponderance alone, engineers are, after teachers, the largest single professional occupation in advanced societies. Yet, though social critics have frequently concerned themselves with the large-scale and long-range implications of complex technology, little attention has been paid to the technologists themselves. Almost since the writings of Veblen (1921) they have been, if not ignored, at least vastly underestimated as a force in contemporary society.

Where engineers have been considered, the context has been broader than the analysis of one particular occupational group. Clearly they are, perhaps above all else, organization men, since to a greater extent than many other professionals they tend to work for large organizations. Accordingly, the perspective adopted by Whyte (1956), that of the common circumstances of all organizational employees, is very relevant to a study of engineers. However, as well as being employees, engineers are professionals, and their technology involves the application of scientific knowledge. Thus it is equally necessary to see them within the framework of the professions, analyses of which must take note of engineers as part of the total picture (e.g. Lewis & Maude, 1952; Millerson, 1964), especially in so far as engineers are representative of the growing new professions in contrast to the traditional models. Similarly, engineering must be related to science, not merely as a body of knowledge but as a social system in its own right, with its own rules of conduct (Barber, 1952; Barber & Hirsch, 1962). The issues that derive from the frequently conflicting demands of organization, profession, and science, suggesting that these are the fundamental perspectives for the analysis of technological professions, are best exemplified in Kornhauser's work (1962), which synthesizes the bulk of the relevant research. Another recent survey dealing with these themes focuses on the professional chemist in the United States (Strauss & Rainwater, 1962).

Apart, however, from a study of the engineering graduates at one American university (Hawkins, Thoma & Lebold, 1959), and an unpublished investigation carried out in Britain that provides useful historical data but is limited to a small sample of contemporary professional engineers (MacFarlane, 1961), the literature of occupational sociology lacks any analysis of this fundamental occupational role comparable with the detailed studies that have been made of other professions.

Some specific educational problems have been receiving attention. For instance, the question of the breadth of education desirable for scientists and technologists was considered in detail by a Leverhulme-sponsored group (British Association, 1961). They concluded that a broader education was required, as indicated by the title of their report, *The Complete Scientist*. To achieve this aim, their recommendations included modification of the A-level school-leaving examination, improvement in the supply of teachers, and reduction of the extreme competition for university entrance. They also suggested that, if adequate breadth and depth of education were to be attained, degree courses might need to be longer. The findings of the Robbins Committee (Ministry of Education, 1963a) are of course highly relevant to the gamut of issues connected with higher education. An attempt to deal with related problems was made by Love (1956), who pointed out some of the shortcomings of engineering education and emphasized that it should include training in logical thinking and scientific method. He also outlined a comprehensive questionnaire that would provide needed information about engineers. Johnstone (1961) carried out an inquiry that was limited to the question of the subjects actually used by chemical engineers in their work, and it served as a basis for a recommended curriculum.

SCOPE OF THE PRESENT STUDY

In the sociological studies we have mentioned engineers tend to be included only in relation to larger problems that are the subject of attention, whereas when specific issues in engineering and scientific education have been investigated, they tend to have an exceedingly narrow focus. The hiatus between these extremes explains the origin and objectives of our study. It was felt that an examination of the nature of mechanical man would be of relevance both for educational policy issues and for the sociology of the professions. Our aims are thus simultaneously pure and applied. In our anatomical study we are concerned not only with dissecting, but also with finding causes of maladies, and tentatively proposing appropriate treatments.

Although our interest is in the engineering profession in general, it was clear that with the limited staff and facilities available and because of the large number of specialist groups in engineering (as discussed in the previous chapter), it would be necessary to confine our study to one of the major branches. Mechanical engineers were chosen as the starting-point not merely because it was a mechanical engineering department that had initiated the research, but also because they constitute the largest branch. The Institution of Mechanical Engineers is the largest of the engineering institutions in Britain and covers the widest range of engineering. Clearly the analysis of one relatively homogeneous group affords a well-defined frame of reference. However, it must not be assumed that the mechanicals are representative of other branches in every respect. For example, there are differences in salary between the various branches of engineering, though these appear to be narrowing (see Chapter 7); and though the proportion of university graduates in all branches is increasing (see Chapter 4), it remains considerably lower among the mechanicals compared with electrical, civil, or chemical engineers.

It is, in fact, the contrast between university graduates and non-graduates among professional mechanical engineers that is at the basis of much of our analysis. Given the two distinct educational streams towards professional qualification (Chapter 4), what are the consequences? Professional engineers include both graduates and non-graduates. To what extent are the two types distinguishable once qualified? Do they do the same kinds of work and receive similar rewards?

The framework of our analysis is provided by the core traits of professions referred to in Chapter 1. In the context of professional *qualifications*, we are concerned with the educational systems that produce engineers. With reference to *autonomy*, our focus entails the depicting of the engineer's working situation. *Commitment* is analysed in terms of the meaning of work, and the extent of involvement with both work itself and with formal and informal professional obligations.

Within and around this framework we deal with those aspects that would be found in almost any occupational analysis. The examination of recruitment attempts to place engineers in the social structure in terms of their social-class origins, and considers the schools they attended and the process of occupational choice. Related general issues are those of the nature of occupational replacement and the extent of fluidity in the social system, the degree to which careers are open to talent.

The chapter on higher education and training begins by specifying the alternative routes to professional qualification. Retrospective evaluations of both the general content of further education and the utility of specific curricula are the major part of the material in this section. Differences between types of graduate, as well as between graduates and non-graduates, are discussed.

Chapters 5 to 8 deal with the engineer at work. First, the work setting is described, in terms of types of industry and organization, the nature of the work, authority systems, and colleague relationships. Then follows an examination of career patterns, starting with first jobs and going on to analyse mobility patterns within and between organizations. Closely related to career patterns are questions of attainment, aspiration, and status, which form the subject of Chapter 7. Income is discussed in this context, as one direct indicator of attainment (other more indirect tokens are looked at in Chapter 9). The assessment of status considers the status problems of the engineering profession as a whole as well as the position of individuals within the profession. To conclude this section, Chapter 8 discusses some aspects of commitment, emphasizing the conflict between professional and organizational orientations, and evaluating the extent of professional involvement outside work itself.

A final section looks at the engineer off duty. Information is presented on leisure patterns, on attitudes to politics and religion, etc., so that the engineer's way of life can be compared in these respects with that of his status counterparts in the broader community. And, of particular interest for an occupational analysis, these data give some indication of the relative importance of work and leisure for the engineer, and of the extent to which the two areas converge.

Whatever aspect of the occupational analysis is involved, there is very little use in attempting to depict the situation of *the* engineer.

Rather, the main interest is in the variations that exist. Differences derive from three major sources: education, age, and career type. A fundamental contrast, as we have noted, is between university graduates and non-graduates. In addition, graduates are differentiated by class of degree attained – those with first-class honours degrees and upper seconds, those with honours degrees of a lower class, and pass-degree graduates.

Our vital concern with future trends, and not merely with the present, suggested a further differentiation in terms of age groups, to show changes over time. The age groups employed for this purpose are: under 35 years; 35 to 44 years; 45 to 54 years; 55 years and over. Since there were fewer engineers in the last two categories, these are combined where appropriate into the category of 45 and over.

The third area of comparison is provided by type of career. The essential distinction is between industrial and non-industrial employment, the latter including education, the armed forces, the civil service, consultancy, and technical journalism. Within industry, three major types provide the basis of comparison – management; operations (including maintenance, planning, production, etc.); and research, design, and development (hereafter referred to as RD and D). As we shall see (Chapter 6), the four career types – management, operations, RD and D, and non-industrial – do not correspond to the details of work functions, but are general categories subsuming the alternative constellations of engineering careers.

Graduate status, age, and career types are our fundamental independent variables, the factors that explain contrasts and trends. There are two major dependent variables employed throughout the investigation, factors that we wish to explain. Financial success is the first of these and involves the most important question: what determines getting ahead? Success is defined by the achievement of the median income for an age group. The 'successful' have attained the median income for their age group and the 'unsuccessful' have not (see Chapter 7). For those under the age of 35 the dividing line for success is £1,200 per annum; for those aged 34–44 it is £1,800; and for those aged 45 and over it is £2,200. The second dependent variable is career orientation, distinguishing between an administrative and a technical preference, a decisive polarity in engineering careers (see Chapter 8). It is based upon the question: 'Assuming the pay would be the same, would you prefer an administrative post or a primarily technical advisory position?'

PROCEDURES EMPLOYED

On the basis of this general outline – covering the areas of recruitment, education, work, and leisure – and after talks with many people interested in the field, a questionnaire was developed (see Appendix 1). It was decided to attempt a nation-wide survey using personal interviews rather than a postal questionnaire because the interview can yield so much more information. Not only is the response-rate likely to be much higher and the sample therefore statistically more reliable, but open-ended questions can be followed up, which would be impossible in a postal study.

The sample was drawn from the current membership list of the Institution of Mechanical Engineers with the aim of obtaining some 1,000 interviews with corporate members and graduate members. Corporate members in this context include full members and associate members. Graduate members must not be confused with university graduates. Henceforth the term 'graduate' used in isolation will refer to a university graduate, whereas 'graduate member' means a member of the institution who has all the paper qualifications for membership, but who, because of age and insufficient practical experience, is not yet a corporate member.

There were four provisos in the selection of the sample:

1. Interviews among graduate members were confined to those who had become graduate members in 1959 or earlier. It was felt that the more recent members, those who had been professionally qualified for less than two years, would not have enough experience of work to be comparable with others in the sample.
2. All members recorded in the membership list as living outside the United Kingdom were excluded from selection in the sample. The reasons for this are obvious. Interviews in Brazilian jungles are inconvenient.
3. No persons who had completely retired from work were interviewed. Not only would questions asking about present working conditions be irrelevant for this group, but only a small number of cases would be involved referring to a time when circumstances were very different.
4. As those members who received their professional education at university were of special interest it was necessary for them to form a sufficiently large group to allow detailed analysis. Because they

constitute a relatively small proportion of the total membership, their numbers were augmented by 50 per cent.

The total number of members of the Institution of Mechanical Engineers, together with sample counts from the membership list for 1961, enabled estimates to be made for purposes of sample selection in accordance with the above criteria. The details of sample selection are shown in Appendix 2. Because of the four selection criteria, the sample is not a random one of all members of the Institution of Mechanical Engineers. Rather, it is mainly confined to those between the ages of 25 and 65, only 3 per cent being 65 and over (criteria 1 and 3), and to those resident in the UK (criterion 2). The disproportionate number of university graduates selected (criterion 4) involved the major departure from representing the typical member of the profession. To compensate for this, appropriate weighting has, where possible, been used in the analysis. The convention adopted is that, whenever a general statement is unqualified, it can be assumed that it applies equally to both graduates and non-graduates, or that it has been weighted to allow for the correct proportion of graduates and non-graduates in the membership of the Institution.

The details of the response-rate are shown in Appendix 3. Interviewing took place in the winter of 1961–62 and the spring of 1962, with a total of 977 respondents – 387 university graduates and 590 non-graduates. This represents a response-rate of 77 per cent, which is lower than that sometimes attained in survey work; it can be partially explained by the length of the interviews, which ran between two and three hours. The most common reason for interview refusals was, in fact, being too busy and not having time for a long interview. The actual reason behind the claim of being busy may well have been antagonism towards busybodies conducting sociological surveys. Indeed, disapproval of surveys was the next common reason for refusal to cooperate.

However, the sample may be assumed to be generally representative of graduate and non-graduate professional engineers, who are above the age of 25, not retired, resident in the UK, and members of the Institution of Mechanical Engineers. For, owing partly to the two-wave method of sample selection (Appendix 2), even the least cooperative sector of the sample – non-graduate corporate members – yielded a response-rate of 70 per cent. It is of interest to note the few available characteristics of those who refused to be interviewed. Refusals were more common among corporate members (27 per cent) than among non-corporate ones (16 per cent); and there were more refusals from non-graduates (26 per cent) than from graduates (18 per cent). While it may appear that younger men – non-corporate members – might have more time on their hands for such frivolous pursuits as answering questions, it would seem unlikely that graduates are less busy than non-graduates. Part of the explanation may lie in that the older non-graduates tend to be, as we shall see, less successful, and consequently perhaps less keen to talk about their careers. More generally, the graduates and the younger men are apparently more tolerant of sociological surveys, and possibly more concerned with the topic of this investigation – the engineering profession.

CHAPTER 3

Recruitment patterns

To begin at the beginning, an occupational analysis needs to concern itself with questions of recruitment. The examination of where practising engineers come from is obviously important today in terms of the implications of recruitment patterns upon problems of scientific manpower and the future needs of the economy. It is also intriguing from a broader, sociological point of view. Given the large numbers of occupations in a complex industrial society, how are they filled? What are the salient dimensions in the process of occupational choice? Some of the fundamental questions concerning recruitment into occupations include: What sectors of the social structure contribute to the composition of an occupation? Are careers open to talent or do class barriers predominate? What influences do various types of school have upon the eventual occupational paths their old boys follow? What factors other than school influences enter into the making of career-choice decisions, at what ages? What is the schoolboy's image of the field he has chosen to enter?

SOCIAL ORIGINS AND SOCIAL CLASS

The social origins of graduate and non-graduate engineers, based upon father's occupation, are quite different (*Table 1*). Both streams of the profession are, however, made up by a majority who have advanced beyond their father's occupational status: 58 per cent of the graduates and 79 per cent of the non-graduates have been upwardly mobile from their fathers' occupational position. Their fathers were neither professionals nor executives, but were in middle white-collar or manual occupations. The largest single aggregate of graduates (40 per cent), however, originates in professional-executive strata, whereas for non-graduates manual working-class backgrounds are most common (45 per cent). Graduates and non-graduates are drawn in almost equal proportions (about a third for each) from middle white-collar groups.

24

Although there is very little direct occupational inheritance, only 4 per cent of the total being sons of professional engineers, the degree of recruitment from the skilled manual category – more than from any other stratum – suggests indirect inheritance. That is to say, even if the father was not an engineer, his being a skilled craftsman provided a technical interest and some knowledge of the world of engineering to be passed on. Indeed, more involvement with engineering matters is likely to be aroused through such channels than through formal educational ones.

TABLE 1   Father's occupation by graduate status

Father's occupation	Graduates N = 387	Non-graduates N = 590
	%	%
PROFESSIONAL-EXECUTIVE	40	20
Professional and high executive	25	12
Managerial and executive	15	8
MIDDLE WHITE-COLLAR	36	34
Inspectoral, supervisory, and other non-manual (higher)	20	11
Inspectoral, supervisory, and other non-manual (lower)	7	17
Routine non-manual	9	6
MANUAL	22	45
Skilled manual	19	35
Semi-skilled manual	3	8
Routine manual	*	2
Retired, unemployed, etc.	2	1
	100	100

* Less than 0·5

Highly related to occupational levels is the extent of parents' schooling, and in this respect also there are differences between graduates and non-graduates. Only 4 per cent of the non-graduates were sons of men who had been to university, as compared with 16 per cent of the graduates. At the other extreme, father's education did not proceed beyond the elementary level in the case of one-third of the graduates and two-thirds of the non-graduates. Both the small numbers who are second-generation university graduates and the large proportions coming from homes where elementary education was typical indicate the extent to which the respondents have advanced beyond their origins.

The extent to which engineering represents an avenue of upward mobility could be seen most clearly in comparison with other occupations and other countries. Unfortunately, there is little information available that is directly comparable. Clements's study of managers in the Manchester area (1958) suggests some similarity as regards social origins between graduate engineers and managers generally; for he reports 37 per cent of managers to be of professional-executive origins, which compares with the 40 per cent of our graduates of similar backgrounds. American findings based on Purdue engineering graduates (Perrucci, 1961), however, show 47 per cent to come from the manual category; this figure closely resembles that for the *non-graduates* in our sample. But a comparison of graduates in the two countries suggests that the engineering profession is more an avenue of mobility in Britain than it is in the United States (Gerstl & Perrucci, 1965).

When older and younger engineers are compared, however (*Figure 1*), considerable changes in the social bases of recruitment of both graduates and non-graduates are revealed over time.

FIGURE 1 Social origins by age

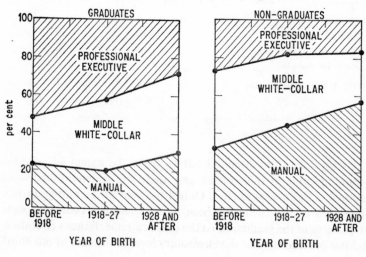

Whereas the oldest non-graduates were mainly recruited from middle white-collar groups (41 per cent), the youngest are mainly working class in origin (57 per cent). Recruitment from the professional-executive group has also declined among the non-graduates (from 27 per cent of the oldest group to 17 per cent of the youngest).

The trend is for middle-class entrants into engineering to follow the path through university. In fact, the younger graduates are increasingly of middle white-collar origins (42 per cent, compared with 25 per cent of the oldest group) and also somewhat more working class (30 per cent, compared with 23 per cent) at the expense of recruitment from the professional-executive strata (which has declined from 52 per cent to 28 per cent). Sons of professionals and executives made up over half of the oldest graduate engineers but constitute the smallest segment among the youngest. There is as much upward mobility among the youngest graduates as among the oldest non-graduates (72 per cent).

Since the proportion of graduates among mechanical engineers does not appear to be increasing rapidly, the trends for the majority of non-graduates are especially important. Changes in the social bases of recruitment are most relevant for their implications concerning the degree of fluidity in the social structure – the extent to which careers are open to talent. The changes over time we have found show an increasingly broad base of recruitment. A more detailed look at the same issue involves not only the question of how much chance a working-class boy has to become a professional, but how much his background matters once he has become qualified. There is more recruitment of engineers from manual backgrounds in the United States than in Britain. But, contrary to the usual stereotype of mobile Americans and class-bound English, the old-boy network would appear to operate less among British engineers than it does among their American colleagues. Whereas American research (Perrucci, 1961) indicates a significant association between father's occupation and job level attained in the engineering profession, our data suggest that social origins have little significance for career attainment beyond their initial critical effect as regards obtaining a university education. Those of white-collar origins are twice as likely as sons of manual workers to attend university, and sons of the managerial-executive class are three times as likely. But, whatever their respective social origins, graduate engineers tend to do better than non-graduates, as shown in *Table 2*.

TABLE 2   Success by graduate status by father's occupation

	Father's occupation			Number of cases
	Prof. exec.	*White collar*	*Manual*	
GRADUATES				
Successful	67%	66%	55%	
Unsuccessful	33%	34%	45%	
Number of cases	154	138	87	379
NON-GRADUATES				
Successful	44%	35%	40%	
Unsuccessful	56%	65%	60%	
Number of cases	118	203	265	586

Among the graduates, sons of those in middle white-collar occupations have just as good a chance of financial success – of attaining at least the median income for their age group – as the sons of professional-executives, in a ratio of 2 : 1. Those graduates from a manual working-class background are less likely to achieve success, but their chances are still better than even, and considerably better than those of non-graduates of high-status origins. For graduates, the major determinant of success is not social background, but the type of university attended and the class of degree attained (see Chapter 4). Ability appears to be at least part of what is involved.

For non-graduates the consequences of social background are even weaker. Though the man from a professional-executive background has some advantage, his chance of success is nevertheless less than even. Curiously, those from a manual background are more likely to succeed than are those from the middle white-collar group. This may well be a reflection of a technical orientation instilled early in life and of the drive and ability of someone who has come up the hard way.

Although background factors have only a limited influence upon the attainment of success within the ranks of the engineering profession, their significance in social life should not be underestimated. To a large extent their operation is not visible. One easily ascertainable indicator of fluidity or rigidity in the class structure is that of marriage patterns, which, on the part of engineers, are seen to be strongly influenced by social origins and show a considerable degree of rigidity. Although all engineers are by their qualifications members of a professional social stratum, the majority do not marry daughters of professionals or executives unless they themselves are of high-status origins. Those of middle white-collar derivation most frequently marry women of a similar background, and those of manual working-class roots also tend to marry their own kind.

Self-placement in response to the question: 'If you had to say which social class you belong to, what would you say?' also reveals the influence of social origins, especially among younger men who are not graduates. Again, although engineers share an identical professional social level, they do not show consensus regarding their self-placement. Half put themselves into the middle category presented to them – an undifferentiated middle class. But, upper- and upper-middle-class labels on the one hand, and lower-middle and working-class ones on the other, correspond to origins and graduate status, and most of all to income levels and type of position. The successful, the managers, and those not in industry more frequently assign themselves the higher-class labels, and the less successful, those in operations and RD and D, are more likely to feel that even the unadorned label 'middle class' is above them. Although they are professionals by the objective criterion of their occupational qualifi-

TABLE 3   Region of birth

Region	%
U.K.	
North	6
East & West Ridings	10
Northern Ireland & North-west	17
North Midlands	4
Midlands	11
East	4
London & South-east	19
South	4
South-west	5
Wales	5
Scotland	9
OTHER COUNTRIES	6
	100

cation, engineers' subjective class identification clearly involves factors additional to occupational niche.

Another aspect of origins is that of the geographical regions from which engineers are recruited (*Table 3*). There do not appear to be any consistent patterns of increasing or decreasing numbers of engineers from particular regions over time. The proportions of graduates and non-graduates are similar for the various areas, but East and West Ridings, the Midlands, and London and South-eastern regions produce more non-graduates, and only Scotland, Wales, and other countries yield a greater propotion of graduates.

SCHOOLS ATTENDED

Type of school attended is obviously a highly significant factor intervening between the effects of social background and subsequent higher education and career contingencies. Changes over time in the types of school attended correspond closely to the changing class recruitment in engineering. It is, of course, largely as a result of the relatively recent changes in educational opportunities in Britain that a wider basis of recruitment has been possible. But the initial point to be noted is the extent to which traditional class lines are reflected and perpetuated through school patterns. As indicated in *Table 4*, among engineers, as in Britain generally, the public school is the

TABLE 4 Type of school by social origin

| Type of school | Father's occupation | | |
	Prof.-exec. N = 270	White collar N = 343	Manual N = 352
	%	%	%
Elementary & secondary modern	2 } 11	12 } 34	19 } 46
Secondary technical	9	22	27
Grammar	43	50	48
Public	43	15	4
Other	3	1	2
	100	100	100

bastion of the upper-middle class just as elementary and secondary modern schools are characteristic of the working class. The grammar school stands as a neutral democratic middle ground, and the secondary technical school might also represent a zone of transition. Age of leaving school similarly follows class lines: by the age of 16, 81 per cent of the sons of manual workers had left school, as compared with 57 per cent of those from white-collar strata and 33 per cent of the professionals' and executives' sons.

Professional mechanical engineers as a whole are more likely to have attended grammar schools (45 per cent) than are comparable groups of managers examined in other studies, who in many cases are doing similar types of work (Clements, 1958; Acton Society Trust, 1956). Very few (8 per cent) had no secondary education. The proportion of all engineers who attended public schools (16 per cent) is lower than that reported for managers in the other studies cited. But graduate engineers, 30 per cent of whom had been to public schools, surpass the managers. However, in comparison with elite occupational groups, for example higher civil servants (Kelsall, 1955) and company directors (Copeman, 1955), 48 per cent of the former and 58 per cent of the latter having been to public schools, even the graduate engineers appear unfavourably.

For the graduates, the major change over time, as shown in *Table 5*, has been the increasing proportion from grammar schools making up the decrease from public and secondary technical schools.

TABLE 5 Graduates and non-graduates by age and type of school

| | No. in group | Type of school attended | | | |
		Sec. tech. & sec. mod.	Grammar	Public independent	Other
		%	%	%	%
GRADUATES					
under 35 years	95	7	63	28	2
35–44 years	179	14	53	30	3
45 years and over	113	14	46	37	3
all	387	12	54	31	3
NON-GRADUATES					
under 35 years	180	42	43	9	6
35–44 years	263	35	44	9	12
45 years and over	147	28	39	16	17
all	590	36	43	11	10

For the non-graduates, the proportion from grammar schools has increased only slightly, the greatest change being increased attendance at secondary technical schools (the proportions from secondary modern and equivalent schools having remained constant). The percentage of non-graduates who attended public schools has also declined.

The increasing numbers of working-class entrants are mainly those who received their education in secondary technical schools. The decline in public-school entrants, on the other hand, corresponds largely with the decline in recruitment from professional classes.

Content of education has also, in accordance with type of school attended, changed over time, more of the younger men having passed ONC, O-level, and A-level examinations. The greatest increase is found in attainment of O level. In the total sample, almost half of the non-graduates had no O-level subjects; likewise, a sixth of the graduates. Half of the graduates had some A-level subjects, but only 6 per cent of the non-graduates had achieved A level. The most common O-level subjects, in order of frequency, were: English, mathematics, physics or chemistry, history or geography or economics, and modern languages.

Three-quarters of the respondents had had their interest in engineering aroused or increased while at school, either through subjects they had studied or through hobbies related to engineering. Owing to the limited availability of engineering subjects in most schools, there were many more references to the impact of subjects such as mathematics or physics than to engineering as such. Engineering subjects were, of course, most important in the case of those who had been to secondary technical schools; but they were also frequently mentioned by those who had attended the major public schools – an indication as to where these subjects are included in the curriculum. In retrospect, however, only a tenth of the respondents would, if they had their education over again, wish to have the opportunity to study engineering subjects in school. In fact, two-thirds could suggest no subject that they felt they had lacked in school. Only foreign languages were mentioned relatively frequently (by a quarter) as a useful addition that the school curriculum should offer.

As we have seen, type of school attended is to a large extent a function of social class. The combined effects of social origins and school influences will explain the likelihood of university attendance (cf. Jackson & Marsden, 1962; Ministry of Education, 1963*a*; Douglas, 1964). The proportions of engineers from various types of school who proceed to university thus range from 3 per cent of those who had had only an elementary education, and a tenth of those who had attended secondary technical and secondary modern schools, to a quarter of those who had been to grammar schools and half of those from public schools. The association between type of school and university education, clearly reflected in these figures for university attendance, is even stronger in terms of type of university attended. All Camford (i.e. mostly Cambridge) graduates had been at either grammar or public schools, three-quarters having attended public schools, mainly boarding-schools. Over two-thirds of provincial university graduates, on the other hand, had been to grammar schools, and less than a quarter were from public schools. Of London graduates, a quarter were from public schools, half from grammar schools, and a quarter from secondary technical and secondary modern schools. The last groups named included many who obtained an external London degree.

For those who go on to obtain a university degree, type of school attended is likely to be a critical factor with regard to getting into university at all. Just as social origins take on less importance once the magic status of university graduate is attained, so does the type of school attended prior to university take on a relatively minor role. In fact, graduates who have been to public schools are no more successful in their careers than those who have been to a secondary modern or technical school or even those with merely an elementary education. And graduates who have been to grammar schools do less well than either public-school or other secondary-school products, perhaps having less pull than the privileged and less push than the underprivileged.

For non-graduates, type of school attended has more direct repercussions upon their careers. Age of leaving school has almost no effect upon the likelihood of achieving success. But the proportions of successful non-graduates range from 35 per cent of those who have been to elementary, secondary technical, or secondary modern schools, to 40 per cent of those who have attended grammar schools, and to half of those who have been to public schools.

Not only do the three types of school correspond with differential rates of success, they also reflect alternative orientations, especially noticeable among the non-graduates, for whom university experience cannot be cited as an explanatory factor. The public-school products tend to be chiefly oriented to administration; at the other extreme, those from secondary technical schools have a strong preference for technical work; and those from grammar schools have only a slight technical preference (see Chapter 8). Public-school products, in fact, very frequently end up in managerial positions, even when they are not graduates, but especially when they are.

Although only a sixth of all mechanical engineers had attended public schools, types need to be distinguished. For within the category 'public schools' different patterns exist. The major distinctions that have proved relevant in previous studies (Clements, 1958; Acton Society Trust, 1956), based upon the work of Jenkins and Jones (1950), are between the nine Clarendon schools, the fourteen other major public schools, other Headmasters' Conference schools, and other independent schools (see *Table 6*).

TABLE 6   Types of public school vs. grammar schools and correlates

			University graduates				
	No. of cases	Sons of prof.- exec.	Weighted	Actually in sample	From Camford	In manage- ment	Suc- cessful
		%	%	%	%	%	%
Clarendon schools[a]	15	87	88	93	65	67	73
Other major public schools[b]	22	76	61	77	82	64	73
Other Headmasters' Conference schools	144	56	47	67	25	46	61
Other independent schools	44	43	28	48	5	39	48
Other grammar schools	459	27	26	44	8	33	49

[a] Clarendon schools: Charterhouse, Eton, Harrow, Merchant Taylors, St Pauls, Shrewsbury, Westminster, Winchester.

[b] Other major public schools: Cheltenham, Clifton, Fettes, Haileybury, Loretto, Malvern, Marlborough, Oundle, Radley, Repton, Rossall, Sedbergh, Sherborne, Uppingham.

The gradation from high to low may be seen clearly in the proportions at the various types of school whose fathers were professionals or executives. By this criterion there is a considerable difference between the bottom category of public schools and grammar schools. However, the most striking aspect of this particular comparison is that, though distinguished in social origins, those who attended public schools that were neither major nor Headmasters' Conference schools emerge as indistinguishable from grammar-school products in subsequent educational and career attainment. For the first three types of public school, on the other hand, considerable gradation persists. It is reflected in the proportions who attended university, in the proportions of graduates who had attended Camford, in the likelihood of attainment of a managerial position, and in the likelihood of financial success.

Because the numbers who attended public school but did not go on to university are small, more detailed analysis of this group is not possible. It is thus difficult to explain the relative influences of public school and university experience upon success and career attainment and orientation. But there can be no question that the combined effect is highly viable.

OCCUPATIONAL CHOICE

Half of the respondents had resolved to become engineers by the age of 15, and by 16 three-quarters had decided upon their future careers. Thus we are dealing with the decisions of schoolboys. In order to obtain detailed information concerning the process of occupational choice, including consideration of such urgent questions as why the ablest science pupils in Britain, unlike those in other countries, show a preference for pure science over technology, the subjects of investigation must be schoolboys themselves. Considerable work in this area is being undertaken (e.g. Jones, 1963; Hutchings, 1963; Institution of Chemical Engineers, 1964). It requires attention to such factors as the connexions between images of occupations that persist in a society, especially among children (see Chapter 7; cf. Mead & Metraux, 1957; Kubie, 1954), and institutional factors – e.g. that engineering subjects, like medicine, are not taught in schools, whereas subjects such as chemistry are (Strauss & Rainwater, 1962), and that careers masters' prejudices reflect relative exposure. In addition, more needs to be known about the mechanisms of socialization into an occupational role. To what extent are the findings concerning American doctors, for example (Merton *et al.*, 1957; Becker *et al.*, 1961), applicable to other professions and other countries?

Recollections of adult respondents about their process of occupational choice also provide some clues. Though grown men cannot be expected to remember – or admit – the details of all the factors that influenced them in choosing their life's work (any more than they can or will remember all factors that led to their choice of wives), those aspects of the decision process that were mentioned in the interviews reveal notable consistencies as well as contrasts. The question used specifically asked for 'the major factors' in the decision to become an engineer, without attempting to distinguish sources of influence from predispositions or opportunities. Since occupational choice is, above all, an ongoing process (Ginzberg *et al.*, 1951), it involves a number of factors simultaneously. As we have seen, when specifically asked about school subjects and hobbies, three-quarters of the sample agreed that these had helped to rouse their interest in engineering. Similarly, home influences and indirect occupational inheritance are reflected in social origins. But the two most salient factors – those most readily volunteered, each by a third of the respondents – were technical predispositions (being 'good with one's hands' or 'mechanically minded') and the influence of particular individuals. These latter were most frequently members of the family connected with engineering, but also included schoolteachers and relatives not in engineering. Graduate engineers made reference to their early academic aptitude at technical things or to a general interest in engineering twice as often as did non-graduates. Non-graduates, on the other hand, emphasized particular opportunities that had lured them, e.g. local industry offered good prospects at the time. Whereas the older engineers came to their work influenced by persons in the field, the younger age groups more commonly stressed their technical predispositions and abilities. This change would appear to correspond with other changes in recruitment that we have noted.

Major motives and influences for becoming an engineer are to a minor extent predictive of directions of specialization. Those currently engaged in RD and D work were the most likely to have been influenced by their teachers and by their predispositions, both to be mechanically minded and to have academic aptitude in scientific subjects. By contrast, those currently employed in non-industrial settings were, although also encouraged by their academic abilities, the least likely to claim having been good with their hands when children. Managers and those in engineering operations resemble each other in emphasizing their initial handiness as well as the influence of relatives. Current degree of commitment (see Chapter 8) to engineering is also related to initial occupational choice factors. While highly committed respondents are as likely to mention technical predispositions or abilities as they are to refer to personal influence or prospects, a low degree of commitment to engineering is significantly related to citing personal influence or career opportunity factors as the major determinants of occupational choice, and especially to choosing engineering because it was the only opening available at the time. A negative motive in choice persists as a negative work orientation. This pattern has immediate practical implications for the most useful guidance that could be given to those interested in engineering careers.

But the amount of negative work orientation or general dissatisfaction found among engineers is, as we shall see, small. Only a fifth of the respondents did not really consider engineering as their first choice. Of alternative considerations, many were never taken very seriously. Moreover, many of the reluctant entrants have seldom looked back, finding that their work has turned out to be most rewarding. At the same time, there are, of course, those who were certain that they wanted to be engineers and did not become unhappy with their choice until it was too late.

Although the image of the engineer in society may be somewhat unclear, one might expect that the schoolboy choosing this career would think exclusively in terms of creativity and making things – whether trains, bridges, or motors. Yet only 40 per cent of the sample recollect having thought exclusively of this aspect of engineering work at the time of their occupational choice. Over a quarter claim to have anticipated a position in management and an eighth had hoped to combine engineering and management from the start (the rest did not consider the problem at that age or do not remember).

The precocious predisposition to management is related to high-status social origins and is more likely among younger respondents. The non-graduates envisaged managerial attainment more frequently than did the graduates. And, among the graduates, those who obtained the best degrees were the least likely to have thought of managerial careers. Similarly, those who had attended grammar schools expressed less anticipation of management careers than those from secondary modern and technical schools, though differences are slight. But those from public schools had the greatest managerial expectations – as high as 40 per cent of those from boarding-schools.

There appears to be a relationship between early anticipation of a managerial position and the actual pursuit of this type of work. Forty-four per cent of those who expected to enter management did so – compared with less than a third of those who did not have this expectation. Similarly, the schoolboy predisposition appears to be related to current orientation. Of those who express an administrative orientation, 42 per cent had anticipated managerial posts, whereas only 19 per cent of those now expressing a technical orientation had originally envisaged management. But rather than assume that youthful expectations tend to be fulfilled, that wishing will make it so, it is more plausible to suggest that those currently in managerial posts with administrative orientations tend to allow their present situation to colour their retrospective glance. It may well be that they have been striving for their managerial rung for a long time, for so long that they have forgotten that at the age of 15 they were in fact more interested in the power of trains than in power over subordinates. Again, as with many aspects of the recruitment process, the actual recruits rather than the established engineers would be more likely to reveal the dynamics involved in occupational socialization.

CHAPTER 4

Higher education and training

ROUTES TO PROFESSIONAL QUALIFICATIONS

Whereas in most countries professional engineering qualifications are awarded and controlled by the state, in Britain they are the responsibility of the major engineering societies. For instance, on the Continent all engineers must have graduated from a state university or a a state engineering school. Most engineers in America, in addition to being college graduates, must also be registered by the state in which they wish to practise, and this involves satisfying the state's requirements for professional engineering qualifications. In Britain, on the other hand, the professional qualification for mechanical engineers is corporate membership of the Institution of Mechanical Engineers, a private organization which has been granted a Royal Charter as a learned society and which is responsible for maintaining standards of entry to the profession. There are several grades of membership, ranging from the junior grade of student to the corporate grades of either associate or full membership, both of which permit the member to practise professionally as a 'chartered mechanical engineer'.

To qualify for associate membership one must be at least 26 years of age, have both satisfactory educational attainments and industrial training, and have held a position of responsibility in industry for several years. In addition, then, to having the requisite industrial training and experience, those seeking professional recognition must either have passed the institution's examinations or hold exempting qualifications.

The main methods of entry to the profession are by means of part-time or full-time courses, together with industrial training before, after, or concurrent with, this education. The various alternatives make a complicated system in the best tradition of British compromise which, in this case, is designed to allow the maximum possibility of entry for those of proven ability. Whereas in many countries there is only one route to becoming a professional mechanical engineer, in Britain there are many.

Part-time courses

Part-time study is usually undertaken with one of two objects in view: either to prepare privately for the institution's examinations, or to obtain exemption from these by attending courses of study that will lead to the Ordinary and Higher National Certificates in Engineering. The latter is by far the most common procedure.

Most of those who study privately take the institution's examinations, which were inaugurated in 1913 to test the general and technical education of candidates who had no exempting qualifications. The syllabus, which is revised periodically, comprises Parts I, II, and III, the first part being the common first examination of similar professional bodies such as the Institutions of Civil and of Electrical Engineers. Parts I and II are strictly on science and engineering subjects, whereas Part III covers industrial administration comprising economics, contract law, and other broad industrial and commercial subjects. Usually the people sitting these examinations are already working in industry and are therefore completing their educational and industrial training at the same time.

The widely used alternative for those already in industry is to study for the Higher National Certificate in engineering, which, with appropriate endorsed subjects, can give complete exemption from the institution's examinations. These National Certificate courses, introduced in 1921, consist of three years' part-time study leading to the Ordinary National Certificate, which exempts from Part I, followed by a minimum of two further years for the Higher National Certificate which, together with appropriate additional subjects, can give exemption from Parts II and III. The standard of the Higher National Certificate is approximately that attained at the end of the first year of a three-year university degree course.

Most of those who take the National Certificates in mechanical subjects are trade or craft apprentices who obtain release from their firms to go to technical colleges one day per week. Some also study at evening classes. By the time that the successful ones have achieved their Higher National Certificate they will also have satisfied the industrial training requirements for corporate membership of the institution.

Full-time courses

Full-time courses are available at technical colleges, at colleges of advanced technology, or at universities, which award respectively National Diplomas, Diplomas in Technology (Dip. Tech.), and degrees.

The National Diploma courses were introduced in 1921 as a full-time alternative to National Certificates. Only recently, however, have the numbers of students taking either Ordinary or Higher National Diplomas increased significantly. Most courses last three years and are of the sandwich type, combining both industrial training and education. An Ordinary National Diploma carries exemption from Part I (except for English), and from Part II on a subject-for-subject basis. A Higher National Diploma can in some cases give exemption from Part III. Some other college diplomas give similar exemption from the institution's examinations.

The Diploma of Technology (Engineering) is a four-year sandwich course usually containing a total of eighteen months' industrial training. The entry standard is similar to the minimum for universities, and the diploma is generally accepted as equivalent to an honours degree. Numbers enrolled have risen steadily from 291 in 1957, the first year of admission to the scheme, to 603 in 1962–63, a year that produced 264 Dip. Tech. awards in mechanical engineering subjects. Holders are normally exempt from the whole of the institution's examinations.

Engineering degree courses at British universities are usually for three years from the intermediate examination, which represents the standard of a boy leaving grammar school at about 18. A University of London external degree can also be taken at some technical colleges. Entry requirements for engineering are usually three science subjects at the intermediate level (the equivalent matriculation or school-leaving qualification is three A-level subjects in the General Certificate of Education examination). A few universities accept the Ordinary and Higher National Certificates in lieu. About 800 university degrees in mechanical engineering are awarded each year. These normally exempt the holders from Parts I and II of the institution's examinations, but a few degree courses that include industrial administration qualify for complete or partial exemption from Part III. After leaving university, most graduates satisfy the institution's industrial training requirements by serving a two-year graduate-apprenticeship course which is designed specially for entrants from university.

CHANGING PATTERNS OF ENTRY

Compared with other engineering institutions the proportion of university graduates among professional mechanical engineers is remarkably low. What is more, the percentage has not risen during the last thirty years. A comparison of the older and younger age groups (*Table 7*) shows that there has been a slight decline in the proportion of graduates despite the increased number of university places in

TABLE 7   Proportions of graduates by age

| | Age group | | | | |
	Under 35	35–44	45–54	55 & over	All
	%	%	%	%	%
Graduates	18	23	23	27	22
Non-graduates	82	77	77	73	78
Total no. weighted	514	791	240	215	1,760

Britain. Although the decline is statistically hardly significant, the absence of any sign of an increase has disturbing implications. It also compares unfavourably with the position in some of the other engineering institutions, in which the proportion of graduates is considerably higher. It is likely that increasing numbers of members who hold a Dip. Tech. or who are graduates from the many new universities will tend to redress the balance in the Institution of Mechanical Engineers, but such influences are only just beginning to be felt.

The most striking change over the years among those qualifying by part-time study has been the large and increasing proportion taking the Higher National Certificate rather than the institution's examinations. This largely explains the decreasing proportion of university graduates noted above, which has occurred despite the increase of university places. Of the non-graduates aged 55 and over, 7 per cent took Higher National Certificate, whereas the proportions for the 35–44 and under 35 age groups were 20 per cent and 32 per cent respectively. This trend is reflected in the high proportion of new associate members of the Institution of Mechanical Engineers who have qualified via the Higher National Certificate route. For instance, of the new associate members admitted in 1960, 65 per cent qualified by Higher National Certificate or Diploma and 24 per cent were graduates.

None of the other non-graduate methods of qualification seems to have changed appreciably over the years, except that the proportions of those taking the Higher National Diploma, which is a full-time course, have increased steadily, from 2 per cent among those over 55 years of age to 9 per cent among those under 35 years old. This is consistent with the present trend in Britain towards full-time higher education; there has been a very marked decrease in the proportions taking evening courses, particularly among the youngest age group: only 11 per cent of those under 35 years took evening courses as opposed to 21 per cent of those aged 35 and over. At the same time there has been an increase in attendance at part-time day courses with decreasing age, from 16 per cent to 45 per cent, no doubt because of the widespread practice whereby firms release apprentices one day per week to study at technical college.

The social backgrounds of part-time day students and part-time evening students are similar, although the latter are somewhat more likely to come from working-class families. Their school backgrounds are also quite similar, but the day students are drawn slightly more often from grammar and secondary technical schools, and the night students from elementary and junior secondary schools. Thirty-seven per cent of each group achieve success. But their orientations and careers differ: the night students are more technically oriented and a higher proportion of them are in fact found working in RD and D (mainly in design); more of the day students have an administrative orientation and end up in managerial and non-industrial posts. The two groups are, however, equally represented in the field of operations and production.

Most of the university graduates (82 per cent) took their engineering degrees through full-time study, the remainder doing part-time London courses. In contrast, less than one-quarter of the non-graduates took full-time courses, their most common method of qualifying being via part-time day courses (43 per cent), with part-time evening classes as the next most likely alternative (31 per cent). Some university graduates (34 per cent of the sample) have already served an apprenticeship and have entered university with Higher

National Certificate; others may have had a year in industry after leaving school.

In engineering, it has been possible to take a University of London external B.Sc. at recognized technical colleges all over the country where suitable laboratory facilities were available. The academic standard of the external London degree is high and comparable with that of the internal degree. Since the growth of Colleges of Advanced Technology there has been a decrease in the number of centres offering the external degree course. Twenty per cent of the graduate mechanical engineers have joined the profession this way, and this proportion does not appear to have changed with time, when current students are compared with the oldest age group.

Although internal and external London graduates produce similar proportions of firsts, seconds, and pass degrees, the external students, who usually come from a lower-status family background, are less successful in later life. Their average income is below that of the internal graduates, 65 per cent of whom attain high success compared with 57 per cent of those with external degrees and compared with 39 per cent of the non-graduates. Possible explanations of this finding might be that the external graduate is handicapped by his social background (the fact that there are fewer external graduates to be found in management compared with internal graduates is consistent with this view), or that the teaching he has received has drilled him to pass an examination which is beyond his true capabilities and is therefore no real index of his ability. The educational and social implications of this situation would appear to merit further study.

There are also some corporate members of the institution (about 8 per cent of the graduates) who originally graduated in a subject other than engineering. They come in similar proportions from London, Camford, and provincial universities, and tend to be mathematicians or pure scientists who have subsequently undergone industrial training and are now holding posts as professional mechanical engineers. Their mode of entry reflects the tradition of British university education which encourages a versatile approach. As might be expected, most of this group are likely to be employed in research or in a non-industrial setting rather than in operations or in management positions.

THE GRADUATE

Analysis by university attended

The analysis of the 387 graduates is based primarily on their classification by university attended. The three university categories are: London, Oxford and Cambridge, and provincial. As *Table 8* shows,

TABLE 8   Universities attended

University	Graduates N = 387
	%
London	35
Cambridge	14 ⎱ 16
Oxford	2 ⎰
Bristol	2
Birmingham	3
Durham	4
Glasgow	7 ⎱ 10
Other Scottish	3 ⎰
Leeds	1
Liverpool	3
Manchester	10
Nottingham	3
Sheffield	3
Cardiff	2 ⎱ 3
Swansea	1 ⎰
Other provincial	4
Foreign	1
Not ascertained	2
	100

a larger proportion of the graduate mechanical engineers came from provincial universities (66 per cent) than from London (35 per cent) or Camford (16 per cent). However, since London is really a collection of universities, Cambridge is the most highly represented individual engineering school, followed by Manchester (which is, in fact, two schools, those of the faculties of engineering and of technology). When the universities are ordered in terms of the proportion of mechanical engineers in our sample to the total student population, then London comes first, Manchester second, and Cambridge third.

The proportion of engineering graduates from London has remained fairly constant over time, being highest among those now in the 35–44 age group. Of those who had attended a provincial university, on the other hand, a considerable proportion (57 per cent) were in the age group under 35, and there were fewer in the age groups over 35. These figures are consistent with the relative rates of expansion of the various universities, the provincial universities having increased their output of engineering students more rapidly than London and Camford. The proportion of Camford graduates, for example, has declined, from a fifth of those aged 55 and over to about one-tenth of those under 35. These trends are likely to continue and their implications must be faced. For instance, will the other universities be able to produce engineering administrators as successfully as Camford?

Class of degree

Degrees are broadly divided into honours and pass degrees, depending in some cases on the marks obtained in the final examinations but more usually on the type of course studied. An honours course is generally more specialized than a course for a pass degree, and of a higher intellectual standard; furthermore, degrees awarded on the successful completion of an honours course are graded by class according to the level of the results obtained by the student.

For purposes of analysis, degrees have been classified in three main groups. These are listed in *Table 9*, which shows the percentages of graduate engineers in the sample in each of the categories.

It is interesting to compare our findings for mechanical engineers with those reported in a PEP survey (1957) of graduates in industry. In the PEP study all second-class degrees were combined in one category, but a comparison of the findings suggests that there are higher proportions of first-class and pass degrees among mechanical engineers than among scientists and technologists generally, and a lower proportion of seconds. The PEP figures for scientists and

TABLE 9   Class of degree

Class of degree	Graduates N = 387	
	%	
1 HONOURS		
First class	26	
Upper-second class	4	
Total		30
2 HONOURS		
Undivided second class	24	
Lower-second class	1	
Third class	7	
Total		32
3 PASS		38

technologists were: 17 per cent had first-class degrees, 30 per cent second-class, and 45 per cent had lower-class honours or pass degrees.

There is evidence of some variation in academic standards when the universities are compared in respect of the proportions of the different classes of degree that they award, as found among the graduate mechanical engineers in our sample (*Table 10*). The data suggest that provincial universities award an unusually high pro-

TABLE 10   Class of degree by university

Class of degree	All graduates[a] N = 387	Camford N = 63	London N = 134	Provincial N = 179
	%	%	%	%
First-class and upper-second-class honours	29	19	26	35
Other honours	33	60	34	22
Pass	38	21	40	43

[a] Includes foreign universities and universities not ascertained.

portion of firsts and upper seconds, almost twice the comparable Camford figure, with London in an intermediate position. Correspondingly, Camford awards an unusually high proportion of lower-class honours degrees and a very low proportion of pass degrees, about half that of the other universities. Since Camford tends to skim the academic cream of the country, these figures testify to the very high academic standards maintained there for first-class honours degrees, and probably for a considerable proportion of other honours degrees. Nevertheless, the few pass-degree graduates from Camford seem to be relatively undistinguished in later life.

Although, as shown in *Table 11*, class of degree appears to be

TABLE 11 Class of degree by type of school

| Class of degree | All graduates N = 387 | Type of school | | |
		Sec. tech. & sec. mod. N = 45	Grammar N = 207	Public N = 122
	%	%	%	%
First-class and upper- second-class honours	29	36	32	21
Other honours	33	18	33	33
Pass	38	47	35	38

related to type of school attended, we must, before jumping to the conclusion that boys who have attended public schools are less likely to obtain firsts than are those from other types of school, remember the previous findings that all universities do not award the same proportion of first-class honours degrees and that the majority of boys from public schools go to Camford, where the chances of a first are lower. Of the total sample, 16 per cent had attended public schools, as was noted in Chapter 3, and 11 per cent went to Camford; thus about 75 per cent of the public-school group graduated from Camford. Nevertheless, when the honours graduates are considered separately for each university, it seems to be the ex-grammar-school boys who consistently attain the highest proportion of firsts at all universities. For example, about 37 per cent of the grammar-school boys who went on to Camford obtained firsts, compared with 15 per cent of those who had been to public schools classed as independent boarding.

Higher degrees
Only 10 per cent of the graduates had higher degrees, 7 per cent having a master's degree and the remaining 3 per cent a Ph.D. or a

doctorate. Full doctor's degrees in engineering subjects are very rare, and the two in our sample were both from Continental universities. Strangely enough, there has been no increase with time in the proportion taking higher degrees. The 'brain drain', though a topic of current concern, is unlikely to provide a sufficient explanation for this finding. Rather, the relative paucity of higher degrees among mechanical engineers may be interpreted as an indication that possession of such a degree is not regarded by British industry as being a particular advantage in this profession. The position for the professional chemist affords a striking contrast: even to be successful as an industrial chemist a Ph.D. is essential.

Class of first degree bears no relation to the taking of a master's degree. Of the twenty-seven people in this category, equal proportions had obtained first-class honours, other honours, and pass degrees originally. At Ph.D. level, however, there is a slight association with standard of first degree: of the twelve graduates who held a Ph.D. degree, five had originally gained first-class honours, five second- or third-class honours, and two had a pass degree.

Type of university attended is more closely associated with the taking of higher degrees than is class of first degree obtained. Master's degrees (both earned and automatic) were least frequent among the Camford graduates (15 per cent) and most frequent among those who had graduated from provincial universities (58 per cent); London graduates occupied an intermediate position (27 per cent) in this respect. The apparent inconsistency of these findings is partly explained by the degree regulations of the various universities: in some cases, possession of an honours degree permits the award of a master's degree automatically after a discreet interval of about two years. Ten of the twelve Ph.D. degrees in the sample were held by graduates of British universities. Of these, six were from London and four from provincial universities; it is interesting to note that none was from Camford. The high proportion of London Ph.D.s is understandable because the university regulations permit all London graduates to qualify for a Ph.D. degree externally, without any residential requirement.

Graduates with higher degrees differ from ordinary graduates in the types of job that they hold; there are also differences between graduates with a Ph.D. degree and graduates with a master's degree. The proportion of postgraduates (38 per cent) in non-industrial occupations, particularly teaching, is twice as high as that among ordinary graduates. Furthermore, within this group of postgraduates those with a Ph.D. are much more highly represented than those with a master's degree, and they tend to be in teaching posts at universities. In contrast, whereas 39 per cent of all the graduates hold positions in management, only 26 per cent of those with higher degrees do so, and, again, they more often hold a Ph.D. than a master's degree. Paradoxically, there are no graduates with a Ph.D. degree in RD and D, and those with a master's degree are represented only in the same proportion as graduates in general. The proportions of higher-degree people in engineering production are also average.

Positions held obviously influence the orientation of respondents. For instance, the proportion of postgraduates having an administrative orientation is only half the proportion for all graduates. However, although postgraduates do not tend to become managers, they achieve a slightly greater degree of financial success than do ordinary graduates, those with a Ph.D. having a better chance than those with a master's degree. Incomes of postgraduates also tend to be slightly higher than those of ordinary graduates.

Differential success-rates of graduates and non-graduates
One of the most significant findings is the large difference between graduates and non-graduates in their chances of success. The assessment of success is no easy matter, for there can be little general agreement upon the ultimate criteria. Since engineers, as we have indicated, are employed in a variety of settings, position in an organization cannot be the measure of achievement. Accordingly we have utilized that crude index, income, as common to all work situations. While we do not make the assumption that virtue is always rewarded, money shows what factors are rewarded. Incomes are closely related to age, therefore our measure of 'success' is based on the median income for an age group. The 'successful' have on this basis attained the median income for their age group and the 'unsuccessful' have not. Actual salaries are listed in *Table 24* and the general question is examined in Chapters 6 and 7.

The effects of various background factors are closely interrelated, as was indicated in Chapter 3. Type of school attended is highly related to social class of origin, and these factors in turn affect the likelihood of proceeding to university and also the category of university attended. The crucial factor affecting success, however, more significant than either family background or type of school attended, is the possession of a good university degree. Whatever their respective social origins, whatever their school background, a much larger proportion of graduate as opposed to non-graduate engineers are successful. Moreover, both type of university and class of degree influence chances of success, as shown in *Table 12*. Whereas 64 per cent of all graduates are successful, only 39 per cent of non-graduates

TABLE 12 Proportions successful by university and by class of degree

University	Class of degree	Percentage successful
Camford	First-class & upper-second-class honours	83
Camford	Other honours	79
London	First-class & upper-second-class honours	71
London	Other honours	69
Provincial	Other honours	67
Provincial	First-class & upper-second-class honours	65
London	Pass	59
Camford	Pass	54
Provincial	Pass	48
All graduates	—	64
Non-graduates	—	39

are. The pass-degree graduate from Camford does little better than his counterpart from a provincial university and less well than the London pass-degree graduate. However, honours graduates from Camford do better than those from London, who, in turn, do better than those from provincial universities. The proportion of successful honours graduates is 70 per cent, compared with 54 per cent of pass graduates. Holders of London external degrees have a lower chance of success (57 per cent) than those having internal degrees (65 per cent). The most important single factor, therefore, for determining success in later life is a university education. Moreover, there is a strong correlation between success and academic ability, indicating that, despite criticisms of university education, it is at least a good method of 'picking the winners'. It could be argued that the group who have succeeded in going to university and obtaining good honours degrees are the most intelligent and would probably have done well even if they had not had a university education. However, this argument may be refuted by comparing, for instance, those from professional families and public schools who have been to Camford with those who have not: whereas 65 per cent of the university graduates are successful, only 37 per cent of the non-graduates are. The inescapable conclusion is that university education is a significant and favourable factor with regard to the likelihood of a successful career. The influence of a higher degree, although not so strong, is also appreciable, but it is remarkable how few engineers have taken higher degrees.

ATTITUDES TO UNIVERSITY EDUCATION

It has already been seen that, in Britain, whether a child goes to university is closely related to his family and social background. Even today, despite the tenets of the welfare state, children from middle-class families do better at school than children of the same intelligence quotient from working-class families, and thus stand a better chance of getting into university. It is therefore of interest to discover the feelings of both graduate and non-graduate engineers towards university education.

Non-graduates

Of the non-graduates in the sample, 40 per cent stated that they had never wanted to go to university to obtain a degree in engineering or any other subject. The remaining 60 per cent would like to have gone to university, 55 per cent to read engineering and 5 per cent other subjects. The retrospective desire to have been to university was strongest among the younger respondents – a finding that may reflect rather that the issue assumes greater importance at this stage of the individual's career than that attitudes are changing over time. In relation to type of schooling, the desire for university education was strongest among those who had attended elementary or junior secondary schools, less strong among those who had been to grammar and junior technical schools, and least strong among those from public schools. It was unrelated to type of career pursued, except that those in production and in RD and D were more inclined to yearn for graduate status (perhaps to get away from these types of job) than were those in management or non-industrial work.

The major reasons, given in 38 per cent of the replies, for not going to university were lack of money and other domestic constraints. The next most common reason (17 per cent of the cases) was lack of the necessary qualifications. Other reasons in order of the frequency with which they were given were: lack of guidance; felt that a practical training would be more useful; served an apprenticeship instead; felt that alternative routes to professional qualifications were preferable; domestic opposition; and, lastly, did not have the ability or temperament for university.

Financial reasons for not attending university are highly related to social background. Half the sons of manual workers mentioned such difficulties, compared with one-third of those from white-collar families and only a fifth from professional-executive families. Similarly, financial reasons were given most frequently by those who had attended elementary and secondary technical schools, less often by those who had been to grammar and secondary modern schools, and least often by the public-school group. The older men mentioned financial considerations more frequently than the younger, a reflection of the better opportunities available today. Correspondingly, the younger men felt that lack of the necessary qualifications was the main reason for their not having taken a university course. Lack of the qualifications required for university entry does not appear to be highly related to type of school attended, except that none of those from boarding schools acknowledged this as his reason.

After their reasons for not going to university had been established, respondents were asked what difference this had made to their careers. Half felt that it had made no difference but 17 per cent claimed that it had made a considerable difference. The younger engineers were less likely than their old colleagues to feel that a university education was a valuable asset. This may indicate either changes over the past two decades in attitudes towards graduate status, or the contrast of occupational experience between younger and older men, or possibly both these factors.

Among the non-graduates there is a close relationship between background factors and attitudes towards university education. For instance, those from a working-class background tend to attach greater significance to the possession of a university degree. Whereas 64 per cent of the sons of professional-executives say that not having a degree has made little difference to their careers, only 42 per cent of the sons of manual workers agree. Because of the close relationship between social background and type of school attended the influence of different types of schooling upon opinions is similar. Those from elementary and junior secondary schools feel most the lack of a degree; it is felt less, in turn, by those from secondary technical, grammar, and public day-schools; and least of all by those from public boarding-schools. As was noted above (p. 52), the lack of a degree does, in fact, make a considerable difference to success even among those from professional families who have been to public school.

The significance attached to not having a university degree varies in different types of work situation and it tends to be emphasized, as might be expected, by individuals who have not achieved success. The advantages of a degree are proclaimed least in managerial and non-industrial occupations and most in RD and D, and in production.

Those who admitted that having no degree had made a difference to their careers were asked to define the difference. The majority replied in terms of four main career themes: (i) they could not go further without a degree; could not get to the top; could not get more responsibility because only university men are considered for promotion; (ii) the choice of jobs open to non-graduates is limited; there are fewer jobs for which they can apply; (iii) there are more opportunities for graduates; (iv) and a graduate earns more. Clearly, the four types of response overlap considerably, but as a group they account for 60 per cent of the replies. The remainder were divided almost equally between an emphasis upon training and knowledge (e.g. with a degree they would have had better or more theoretical training); references to status and prestige (e.g. they were not able to get professional status soon enough; a degree conferred certain social advantages); and a general feeling which was most frequently expressed as 'it made a difference which is difficult to explain'.

Career themes are mentioned to the same extent at all age levels, but comments appreciating the training and knowledge that may be acquired from a university course are most frequently made by the younger and seldom by the older respondents. The status factor also seems important to the young, and particularly to those who come from a lower-status background, i.e. sons of white-collar and manual workers.

Career themes are given prominence at all income levels except the highest. The non-graduate who earns over £3,000 per annum cannot say that not going to a university has prevented him from getting ahead, but he still feels a certain deprivation of status. Status and training, then, are mentioned more frequently by those with high success, and career factors by those with low success. It is obviously those who feel status deprivation or who have not achieved success who have responded positively to this particular question about feeling the lack of a university degree.

In terms of career type, it is noteworthy that managers mostly stress the training and educational function of a degree course and are least likely to mention status. Graduate status undoubtedly gives an entrée to certain jobs which would be barred to non-graduates. Once the individual has secured such a post, however, his subsequent achievement will depend largely on his ability; thus in later life the well-established manager may have forgotten or may prefer to ignore the fact that his degree provided him with the key to a successful career.

As a check on the consistency of expressed attitudes, respondents were also asked whether they regretted the fact that they had not been to a university. The pattern of replies was very similar to that received to the earlier question about the effects of not having had a university education, but the regrets were greater than the ill effects on careers actually experienced.

The non-graduates are split three ways: those who have no regrets (51 per cent), those who feel some regrets (29 per cent), and those who keenly regret their lack of a degree (17 per cent). Again, it is the younger men who express less regret, perhaps because they had more choice in the matter than the older men, although it is probable that their regrets may increase as they get older. Expression of regret is, in conformity with the previous responses, related to background, type of school, and achievement of success; similarly, regrets are felt most by those in RD and D but, contrary to the previous pattern, they are felt least by those in production. Those who express the greatest regrets on this issue are most likely to be thinking of a university degree specifically in terms of its effects on career prospects; those whose regrets are not so great tend to refer more to the status or educational aspects.

E

Comparison of non-graduates' and graduates' views

For an overall comparison of graduates' and non-graduates' attitudes to university education, it was pointed out to all respondents that a recent Engineers' Guild survey showed that university graduates earned more than non-graduates, and they were asked to say what they thought were the reasons for the difference in earnings. The most significant factor about the replies was that 63 per cent of the non-graduates gave reasons connected with the prestige of graduates, whereas 80 per cent of the graduates referred to the superior ability and training of people educated at university. The contrast between the two sets of attitudes, although quite understandable, is very marked. Of the various prestige reasons given by the non-graduates, the most common was that employers favour graduates because of the snob value of a degree; among the graduates, the points most frequently put forward were that a university training teaches individuals how to think clearly and that the courses offered are broader and at a higher level than those available elsewhere.

CURRICULA – REAL AND IDEAL

Given the persisting shortage of engineers in Britain in the face of increasing demands for their skills, a basic concern is to ensure optimum use of the period available for formal education. Do the existing courses equip embryo mechanical engineers to cope effectively with current and future technological needs? To answer this question, it is first necessary to find out what types of educational curriculum professional engineers have experienced and how well these have fitted them for their task.

Extent of specialization

Major contrasts in educational patterns are found between graduates and non-graduates and also between graduates of different universities. The main types of specialization among those in our sample of professional mechanical engineers are listed in *Table 13*.

Unfortunately, it is not possible to distinguish those who started out by studying another field of engineering and then switched to mechanical engineering, but it is clear that more than half the sample were trained in subjects other than mechanical engineering. The proportions of graduates and non-graduates who studied mechanical engineering are remarkably similar, but where other subjects are con-

TABLE 13 Fields of engineering studied

Fields of engineering studied	Non-graduates N = 590	Graduates			All N = 387
		London N = 134	Camford N = 63	Provincial N = 179	
	%	%	%	%	%
Mechanical only	47	47	21	49	44
Also trained in:					
Civil	7	19	48	17	23
Electrical	30	34	49	35	37
Marine	10	2	3	7	4
Chemical	4	2	5	2	3
Aeronautical	6	5	9	6	6
Automobile	7	–	3	3	2
Mining	1	1	–	–	–
Other speciality	5	2	8	1	2
General	–	–	13	–	2
Total[a]	70	65	138	71	79

[a] Multiple answers

cerned the differences are considerable. For instance, in civil and to a lesser extent in electrical engineering, relatively more graduates than non-graduates specialized. For most other specialities the proportion of non-graduates is greater than that of graduates.

When the universities are compared in respect of engineering courses, the lack of specialization at Camford is unique. Most other universities offer a degree course specifically in mechanical engineering which, although broadly based, is not as wide as the Camford engineering science course.

In terms of changes with time, there appears to be an increasing tendency to study mechanical engineering only: 37 per cent of the over 55 age group compared with 50 per cent of those under 35 studied mechanical engineering only. Class of degree is not associated with the pursuit of particular specialities, apart from an over-representation of first-class-honours graduates among those who have an aeronautical training. However, a more significant finding is that narrow specialization seems to be associated with a lower-class degree. Of those with firsts, 38 per cent specialized in mechanical engineering only; of those with seconds, the proportion rises to

43 per cent; and among those with a pass degree it reaches 49 per cent. Interpretation of these figures can be only tentative: they may suggest that it is more difficult to obtain a good degree in mechanical subjects only than in a general engineering course. They may be partly explained by the unusually high proportion of seconds at Camford, where the course is broadly based.

Extent of specialization is also related to type of career and achievement of success. Those now in management positions tend to have a less specialized background than those in other types of work. Those with lower incomes, those who have not achieved high success, are more likely to have been trained in mechanical engineering only.

A broad range of engineering subjects is presented in *Table 15* (p. 60 below). Not all of these, however, are studied by all students. It is of interest to note that those subjects which were least often taken were automatic control, statistics, work study, report writing, and production engineering. About half the sample had never studied any of these, the proportions varying little with age or between graduates and non-graduates. The main differences were that more non-graduates had studied production engineering, work study, and industrial economics, but more graduates had studied metallurgy, structures, vibrations, thermodynamics, and fluid mechanics.

The main differences between universities seemed to be that, generally speaking, provincial universities devoted more time to statistics and work study, Camford more to strength of materials, and London more to electrotechnology.

In addition to the strictly engineering and science subjects studied, 72 per cent of the non-graduates and 41 per cent of the graduates had taken non-technical subjects at college or university (*Table 14*). Engineers educated at technical colleges are more likely to read non-engineering subjects. The major difference between graduates and non-graduates is in the proportions who studied English: this may be explained by differential attainments in this subject at entry to higher education. For all groups, industrial administration is the most frequently studied of the non-engineering subjects: the particularly high proportion among non-graduates is probably because it is an obligatory requirement for the Associate Membership examination.

Graduates of provincial universities are more likely to take subjects in all the above categories than are those who attended London and

TABLE 14 Non-engineering subjects studied at college or university

Subject	Graduates N = 387	Non-graduates N = 590
	%	%
English	5	35
Modern languages	11	15
Economics	13	18
Costing, etc.	7	16
Industrial administration	22	49
Other	2	6
Total[a]	60	139

[a] Multiple answers

Camford. For instance, over half the provincial graduates read at least one non-engineering subject, as compared with one-third of the London graduates and one-quarter of those from Camford.

The proportion who studied English and industrial administration is much greater among those under 45 than it is for the older respondents. On the other hand, modern languages were more frequently studied by those over 45.

Not only is the proportion of engineers pursuing non-technical subjects small, but the length of time devoted to such subjects is, apart from the field of languages, usually not longer than one year. Engineering education cannot therefore be said to be very broad in so far as it includes liberal studies, but this is largely because of the relatively short length of the courses in Britain and the need to reach high standards in engineering subjects.

Engineering education in practice

There can be little question that the optimum course is that which is of maximum benefit to the engineer in his subsequent career. One of the aims of this survey was to assess the relative usefulness of the subjects studied. An attempt was made to compare respondents' subjective opinions as to the value of the various subjects they had studied with the frequency of their use of these subjects in their work. An evaluation of the usefulness of chemical engineering courses had already been successfully made by Edgeworth Johnstone (1961). It was decided, therefore, to make a similar assessment of the practical value of mechanical engineering education, based on frequency of use of the subjects studied, and to see how the usage ratings of subjects compared with engineers' estimates of their value.

Respondents were asked to evaluate the twenty-two subjects listed in *Table 15*, and also to state how often they had used their knowledge of them during the previous five working days. As the subjects were chosen to correspond with the various broad titles to be found in college and university curricula, some ambiguity and overlap are inevitable, particularly, for instance, with reference to vague yet

TABLE 15   Value and utilization of subjects studied

| Subject | Ranking | | % of sample who: | |
	Usage	Subjective	used subject more than once in 5 days	deemed subject essential
Mathematics	1	1	70	74
Engineering drawing	2	2	60	70
Technical report writing	3	5	48	50
Applied mechanics	4	3	43	60
Properties and strength of materials	5	4	41	55
Industrial administration	6	11–12	39	27
Production engineering	7	14	31	25
Principles of electricity	8	9	30	34
Fluid mechanics	9	7–8	28	37
Heat engines	10	7–8	25	37
Theory of machines	11	6	24	39
Metallurgy	12	16	23	21
Automatic control	13	18	22	16
Thermodynamics	14–15	10	21	32
Heat, light, sound	14–15	11–12	21	27
Electrotechnology	16	17	20	17
Statistics	17	21	19	10
Fuel	18	15	18	23
Work study	19–20	19	16	14
Theory of structures	19–20	13	16	26
Vibration	21	20	10	13
Foreign languages	22	22	8	4

widely used headings like applied mechanics. The findings are sum-marized in *Table 15*. The degrees of subjective ranking were: essential; very useful; moderately useful; of little or no use. First-class-honours graduates tended to rate all technical subjects more highly than did second-class-honours graduates who, unexpectedly, rated technical subjects lower than did pass-degree and non-graduate men. This finding may be a consequence of the tendency for graduates with second-class degrees to be found most frequently in managerial positions where extensive technical knowledge is less important.

Correlations between subjective assessment and actual usage were fairly close, fourteen of the twenty-two items being within three places on the two lists. There was general agreement on the rankings between graduates and non-graduates under the age of 54. The older men, however, rated most technical subjects more highly, although they did not use them as frequently as their younger colleagues. Presumably, although the older men had tended to become ad-ministrative, in their longer careers they had encountered more types of engineering problems and realized the need for wide technical knowledge.

Mathematics and applied mechanics were used most frequently by the younger engineers and those in RD and D. The fact that it was non-graduates and the young who tended to use these subjects most often suggests that the mathematics and mechanics entailed were of a fairly elementary standard. The older men used mathematics less often, probably because they have administrative positions.

As would be expected, engineering drawing was used most fre-quently by young non-graduates, who tend to be employed in draw-ing offices in their first post (see Chapter 6). Except for those under 35, technical report writing was used frequently by all, and particu-larly by first-class-honours graduates. Properties and strength of materials were used most in RD and D and seemed to be associated with low success. Production engineering was used most by non-graduates; and work study, industrial administration, and economics were all used most by the high-success types in management, sales, and costing.

Foreign languages were used least often and then mainly by graduates and those in management, particularly the 45–64 age group.

Of the 20 per cent of graduates and 11 per cent of non-graduates who had studied aeroengineering, most seemed to be currently employed in a different field because only one-quarter of the graduates and one-half of the non-graduates used the subject more than once a week.

When the two rank orders are examined (*Table 15*), it is seen that several subjects, such as industrial administration, production engineering, automatic control, and statistics, were considerably (four or more places) higher on the usage list than on the subjective one. Others, such as theory of machines, thermodynamics, heat, light, and sound, and theory of structures, were in contrast overrated; that is, they were lower on the usage list. One must be careful about attaching too much significance to such discrepancies because it is not easy to assess either rank or usage accurately. Moreover, one's usage of a subject and opinion of its importance will depend on one's familiarity and expertise in the field. For instance, the newer subjects such as automatic control and statistics may not have been studied by the older engineers; for this reason, their usage would be expected to be relatively low and this might affect their subjective rating.

Given these limitations, however, it is fairly safe to accept the validity of the assessment in respect of the subjects at the top of the list. The broad field of mathematics was quite clearly the most highly evaluated subject for all classes and age groups, followed by engineering drawing, applied mechanics, and properties and strength of materials. It is noteworthy that technical report writing also comes within the first six, as does industrial administration.

If these rankings can be relied on and if they are unlikely to change to a marked degree during the next few years, they might serve as guidelines with regard to the allocation of time among the various subjects within existing curricula. It is clear, for instance, that the already acknowledged importance of mathematics, mechanics, and strength of materials has been confirmed, but that more time should be devoted to technical writing and to the broad field of communication involving both writing and drawing. It is not sufficient for engineers to have good ideas; they must be capable of convincing other people. The data suggest further that more courses should give increased time to industrial administration.

Towards the optimum course

Respondents' opinions were also sought on the objectives of an ideal course in engineering. Despite the seemingly different functions of technical colleges and universities, given four objectives to rank in order of importance for an ideal course, graduates and non-graduates of all ages were agreed on the following order:

1 To teach the fundamentals of the main engineering subjects.
2 To teach students the technique of scientific method and to stimulate them to think about their subject.
3 To teach specific skills, e.g. drawing, engine tests.
4 To teach special branches of engineering, e.g. automotive engineering.

From an analysis of subjective judgements, the general opinion about the content of the optimum university engineering degree course, and the amount of time to be allocated to each section, are shown in *Table 16*. It is significant that it was the older engineers who most frequently stressed the need for broader studies: their recognition of the value of a wider education may stem from their experience of management and administration.

The greatest difference between *Table 16* and existing university courses in Britain is the large share of time, almost a third, suggested for English, technical report writing, foreign languages, industrial administration, economics, and social science. At the moment, all but the last three are very much neglected. It must be admitted that although present courses at universities and elsewhere seem broadly satisfactory in their technical content, they do not produce complete scientists having breadth of education in non-technical fields or skill in technical communication. The ability to understand men, like the ability to understand machines, can to a certain extent be learned on the job, but the task is easier if one has a grasp of the principles beforehand. This aspect of engineering education is gravely deficient.

For comparative purposes, the recommendations of the American Grinter Committee (1955) have been included in *Table 16*. It is interesting to note the similarity between these and British opinion. An essential point is, however, that the American recommendations are based on a four-year course, whereas the British suggestions relate to the normal three-year university course. *The Complete Scientist* (British Association, 1961) recommends more time for non-scientific subjects in a first-degree course, especially in the communication group, i.e. English and foreign languages. It is recognized, however, that this would be possible only in a four-year course and is unlikely to be attempted for the next fifteen years, during which pressure on university places in science and technology

TABLE 16   Ideal university course

Subject	Per cent of total time Present study	Grinter Committee[a]
English and humanities	7⎫	⎫
Technical report writing	7⎬ 21	⎪
Foreign languages	7⎭	⎬ 30
Industrial administration, economics, and social science	10	⎭
Fundamental sciences: mathematics, physics, chemistry	23	25
Basic engineering sciences, e.g. strength of materials	27	25
Design engineering	13 ⎫	⎫
Speciality engineering, e.g. instrument or textile	6 ⎭	⎬ 25
	100	105[b]

[a] For comparison, figures from an American evaluation have been included. The general agreement is remarkable, albeit 10 of the 30 per cent ascribed by the Grinter Committee to liberal studies referred to optional subjects, which might be in engineering or in fundamental sciences. It must be emphasized that the American figures are for a four-year course of study, whereas the British figures relate to a three-year course.

[b] Committee stated about $\frac{1}{3}$, about $\frac{1}{4}$, etc.

will continue to be especially strong. Thus the evidence suggests that British university courses should devote more time not only to humanistic studies, but also to technical writing and the broad problem of communication. If this is to be achieved without sacrificing academic standards in engineering subjects, it is clear that university courses in Britain must be extended. The practical problem is whether the extra time should be gained by lengthening the undergraduate course to four years, or by adding a postgraduate year for those of ability, as suggested by the Robbins Committee (Ministry of Education, 1963a). If the current level of response to engineering postgraduate courses is any guide, it would seem that the second solution would fail through lack of support. It may therefore be more practicable, although more expensive, to extend the undergraduate course to four years.

Respondents were asked to indicate additional subjects that they would like to have studied, both at school and later. Only a third would have liked additional subjects at school, and of these foreign languages were the most popular, particularly among the non-graduates and those in RD and D.

More than half had no desire for additional engineering subjects in their period of higher education; among the remainder, the most popular subject was electrotechnology, which non-graduates wanted twice as often as graduates. There was a general tendency for men over 55 to express less need for most subjects. Just over half the sample had no wish to have studied additional non-engineering subjects in higher education. The most emphatic respondents were those over 55 and those in non-industrial careers. On the other hand, more than half the pass graduates would like to have studied more subjects, the most popular ones being languages, economics, and social science.

EVALUATION OF HIGHER EDUCATION AND TRAINING

Although most respondents were broadly satisfied with their education there was considerable dissatisfaction with industrial training. About 70 per cent of graduates and non-graduates thought that engineering education at universities and technical colleges was very or fairly adequate. There was little difference of opinion between graduates and non-graduates, the successful and the unsuccessful, and respondents in different types of career. Personal experience in one form of education did, however, introduce a slight bias in favour of the known compared with the unknown system. Despite the high general level of satisfaction, only one-quarter of the comments on universities and technical colleges were entirely satisfactory. The general criticisms were that courses at universities were too academic and those at technical colleges too vocational. The most commonly quoted advantages were, for the universities, that they offered a more complete and broadly based education; for the technical colleges, that they offered a more practical course in close contact with industry. Obviously, if carried to extremes, either of these tendencies could be disadvantageous. One-third of the remarks about the technical colleges and two-thirds of those about the universities were unfavourable: the most common criticisms of technical colleges were that time was too limited, courses were too vocational, and the teaching was sometimes poor; of universities, that courses were too academic and specialized, and remote from industry.

Half the respondents thought that best use had not been made of the time spent on industrial training, the most frequently given reasons being the lack of planned instruction, poor supervision, and the limited nature of the practical experience. Graduates were slightly more critical, but the size of firm in which training took place had no influence upon opinions.

Most agreed that works training was best obtained during the period of academic education: most of the non-graduates and about half of the graduates had in fact gained their industrial experience in this way. If this was not possible, then industrial training should be obtained before but not after the period of academic education. One-third of the graduates had been trained by this method. The fact that most of the sample had received their industrial training during their period of academic education is probably because it is the most common method for non-graduates taking the Higher National Certificate or the institution's examinations. This explanation is supported by the evidence that those who were educated and trained concurrently tended to be less successful. This is not a criticism of the method of education and training; rather, it reflects the fact that the people concerned rarely went on to university and therefore stood less chance of becoming successful.

Most of the respondents had served an apprenticeship of some kind: one-third of the graduates had served a five-year craft apprenticeship, and one-third a two-year graduate apprenticeship. Lack of an apprenticeship training seemed to make little difference to salary, success, or career type. By European standards, five years spent in apprenticeship are too long and three years are adequate for learning all but the most exacting crafts. Is a two-year graduate apprenticeship too long, or is it time well-spent? In many cases it appears that better use could be made of the time, and in some cases graduates get such a poor impression of industry that they are encouraged to seek non-industrial posts when their training is complete. This is an unsatisfactory state of affairs, for which industry must be held responsible. To do them credit, many firms are developing excellent industrial training schemes, but there is in general much room for improvement. Large organizations should be quite capable of looking after themselves, but the very large number of small firms are likely to have difficulties. Singly, they are unable to give trainees the width of experience necessary, and it is only by collaborating with other small firms that they will be able to operate satisfactory training schemes. An excellent group training scheme has been pioneered by the electrical engineering firms in Scotland.

CHAPTER 5

Work setting

In considering the engineer's world of work it is necessary to delineate the nature of careers connected with this occupational role. But before an analysis of career patterns is attempted it is desirable to examine the setting of employment. The analogy of the theatre may be appropriate: careers are like a play in which occupational roles are enacted; but the stage must be set in advance. Our setting involves first of all the organizational context: where is it that the engineer is employed? Here, we will be concerned with the array of employers – industrial and other, large and small. Second, what does the occupational role comprise? Just what is it that the engineer does in his job? Whatever the nature of the role in its various organizational contexts, it involves social relationships. This is the third aspect of the setting: How much authority does the engineer manifest? Who are his superiors and subordinates? To what extent is he involved with professional colleagues? Finally, having set the scene with content, people, and places, the remaining area is that of time: How much work does the engineer do and when does he do it? These initial questions are, of course, formulated in an oversimplified manner. For the answers, as we have previously indicated, must be in terms of the variations among engineers and the correlates of age, graduate status, career type, and success.

ORGANIZATIONAL SETTING

Most professional mechanical engineers – almost two-thirds of the sample – are employed in commerce and private industry. One-seventh work in nationalized industries, in the United Kingdom Atomic Energy Authority, and in public utility undertakings and with local authorities (other than teaching). The rest, not working in industry, include: 8 per cent with universities and technical colleges, 7 per cent in the civil service, 4 per cent in consultancy, 2 per

68

cent in the armed services, and the remainder in such careers as technical journalism.

This distribution is similar for each age group, though older men are more frequently found in non-industrial employment. (The contrast of age groups will be considered in more detail in the section on career patterns that follows.) Differences between graduates and non-graduates are also minor. However, in commerce and industry, the proportion of non-graduates is slightly greater (66 per cent vs. 62 per cent graduates) and that of first-class graduates is considerably less. Conversely, in non-industrial posts, mainly in universities and technical colleges, more graduates than non-graduates are found. A large proportion of these are first-class graduates but, curiously, many pass graduates are included as well. In all of these organizational settings the ratio of successful to less successful engineers is almost equal, except for lower financial success being associated with universities and technical colleges, and a better than 2 : 1 success-rate with consultancy.

Mechanical engineers are widely spread among a large number of industries, with concentrations in mechanical equipment (23 per cent), electronic and electrical firms (13 per cent), and chemicals and plastics (11 per cent). Other industries, in descending order of the proportions of the sample they engage (from 7 per cent down to 1 per cent), are: aircraft, metals, extraction, power, automobile, construction, shipbuilding, materials, food and drink, and railways.

Younger men are more likely to be employed in aircraft, electrical and electronic industries, mechanical equipment firms, and in power (nuclear, atomic, and water). There is however, on the whole, little variation by age among the industrial types.

The proportions of graduates and non-graduates are also surprisingly similar in most industries. Non-graduates are somewhat more prevalent in automobile manufacture, metal production, and mechanical equipment firms. The chemical industry stands out in being the only one in which graduates appear in greater proportions than non-graduates: it contains the highest ratio of first-class graduates, and at the same time favours the pass graduate compared with the ambiguous lower-second-class or third-class man.

Concentrations in managerial posts, as opposed to those in operations or those in research, design, and development, vary from industry to industry. Singular patterns are evident in aircraft, with more men in RD and D than in other types of work, and in mechanical equipment firms, with the greatest concentration in managerial ranks. In most industries, the chances of attaining success are almost even. Being successful is most common in chemicals, largely because of the higher success-rates of graduates, in electrical (but not electronic) firms, and in metal production. The less successful rewards tend to accrue in aircraft (for RD and D work), in railways, and in mechanical equipment.

Whatever the work setting in terms of organizational or industrial type, most engineers work for large establishments; only 3 per cent of the total sample are self-employed. Nearly three-quarters work in units with 500 or more employees, 16 per cent in medium-sized settings (100–499 employees), and the rest in small organizations with fewer than 100 employees. Whereas all age groups are equally represented in medium-sized establishments, younger men are more likely to be found in large organizations, and the smaller ones employ a disproportionate number of older men. Small and large organizations employ similar proportions of graduates and non-graduates, but the type of work done in these contexts differs. Working in operations and in RD and D is more common in the large establishments; the smaller settings tend to have more positions in administration and to include consultancy firms. This contrast explains the age differences and also indicates why those associated with smaller concerns are more likely than not to be successful.

The type of production process with which engineers in industry are involved provides a useful summary description of the technological nature of the types of work pursued. The sample as a whole is fairly evenly divided between unit, small-batch, large-batch or mass, and process production industries. Unit production refers to making either simple or technologically complex units to customers' orders; small-batch to small runs of a product; large-batch or mass to the use of assembly lines in the production of long runs; process to automatic controls (cf. Woodward, 1958). Many industries are characterized by only one type of production; others are spread over the whole range of processes (see *Figure 2*). Thus, shipbuilding tends to be unit work; aircraft, small-batch; automobiles, mass production; and extraction, process production. In contrast, the electrical industry embraces all types of process and metal manufacture covers the three larger types. The power industry is unique in being represented at both extremes.

Although, as has been noted, the proportions of graduates and

FIGURE 2 Production process by type of industry

	Unit	*Small-batch*	*Large-batch/ Mass*	*Process*
Construction	**			*
Extraction				***
Aircraft		***		
Automobile			***	
Shipbuilding	***			
Railways	*	**		
Chemicals, plastics			*	**
Electrical	**	*	*	*
Electronic	**	**		
Metal production		**	**	**
Materials			*	**
Mechanical equipment	**	**	*	
Power	**			**
Food and drink			**	**

Key: * = 20–32%
      ** = 33–65%
      *** = 66%+

non-graduates are similar in different industries, this is not the case when production processes are compared. The proportion of graduates is smallest in large-batch or mass production (17 per cent), increases for small-batch (19 per cent), again for unit production (21 per cent), and is greatest in the case of process production (24 per cent). The relationship between type of process and manpower requirements is indicated in that not only the proportion of graduates but the proportion of first-class graduates is highest in process industries. Unlike other production types, but as in the chemical industry, process production also employs more pass graduates than lower-second-class and third-class men.

The use made of engineers differs in each of the production types. Unit production has comparatively few in managerial posts, but the highest proportion in RD and D. Small-batch processes employ the highest proportion in management – almost half – and the smallest proportion in production. Process industries, by contrast, have few in management or RD and D and the highest proportion in production work; in large-batch and mass production, the three work functions indicated are evenly spread.

F

TYPES OF WORK

The actual work performed by the professional mechanical engineer has been analysed in terms of the *main* type(s) of work done as well as in terms of the amount of time devoted to the various functions most generally subsumed by the engineer's role, and the amount of authority exercised.

Most notable with reference to the main type of work performed, as shown in *Table 17*, is the sheer amount of variety. Few engineers

TABLE 17   Main type(s) of work function by graduate status and industrial career type

Type of work	Graduates N = 387	Non-graduates N = 590	Industrial career type		
			Management N = 340	Operations N = 273	RD & D N = 217
	%	%	%	%	%
Construction	12	13	12	19	9
Production/ operations	15	19	22	26	8
Maintenance	12	14	17	19	3
Testing and inspection	12	17	16	20	10
Design	29	43	28	38	70
Research and development	32	30	24	33	48
Work study, op. res.	9	11	12	12	5
Sales	11	11	23	5	3
Costing and finance	15	15	23	12	9
Administration, technical	51	45	82	39	19
Administration, non-technical	26	18	41	9	6
Teaching and training	21	15	11	9	6
Other	3	4	1	2	1
Total[a]	248	255	312	243	195

[a] Multiple answers

work in only one of the functions indicated, and many are concerned with more than two. The contrast between graduates and non-graduates is most marked in the case of design, an activity performed by a much larger proportion of non-graduates. Functions which might be most generally labelled operations – construction, production/operations, maintenance, and testing and inspection – tend more to be the work of non-graduates. In contrast, administrative work, whether of a technical nature or not, is more frequently in the hands of graduates.

The major types of work performed in industry have, for much of our analysis, been grouped into three large categories – management, operations, and RD and D – on the basis of the one function that predominates. But, as the second half of *Table 17* shows, these types are by no means 'pure'. Thus, those labelled 'operations' are mainly concerned with the first four types of work listed, but they also do a considerable amount of design, research and development, and technical administrative tasks. Those in management, on the other hand, are most widely dispersed over all types of work, whereas those in RD and D are the most specialized.

Examination of the proportion of engineers spending time upon various work functions indicates the diversity of the engineer's job even more dramatically than does the spread of major work functions. This information is summarized in *Table 18*: it shows a similarity between graduates and non-graduates, the major disparities being in the proportions of non-graduates spending time on design, testing, and routine office work, and of graduates spending time on non-technical administration. Not shown in the table is the fact that, of those graduates devoting time to research and development, design, and teaching, the best graduates spend the most time in these areas, which is not the case in any other work function.

Judged by the spending of any time upon particular functions and in terms of those who devote at least a seventh of their total time to the functions, five types of work are seen to predominate: technical administration, design, research and development, routine office work, and non-technical administration. The last two clearly indicate that a majority of engineers spend time on activities that are not, in the technical sense of the term, engineering. Whatever their specialization, a majority find themselves involved in considerable office work and administration. Furthermore, although only a small proportion of the profession are specifically in research or design and

TABLE 18 Proportions of graduates and non-graduates spending any
time 'on various functions, and proportions of total sample
spending at least 15 per cent of their time on these functions

| Type of work | Time spent by: | | At least 15% |
	Graduates	Non-graduates	time spent by:
	%	%	%
Construction	17	22	8
Production	22	28	10
Maintenance	20	25	9
Testing and inspection	28	37	8
Design	55	68	36
Research and development	54	55	28
Work study and operations	21	22	4
Sales	24	23	10
Costing and finance	40	41	10
Technical administration	75	72	35
Non-technical adminis-			
tration	45	36	19
Routine office work	54	62	18
Teaching	20	14	8
Training	15	13	4
Total	490	518	207

development, it is significant to note that a sizable majority from
both management and operations nevertheless do *some* work in
these areas.

The amount of time respondents spent in various functional areas
of engineering work gives no indication of the level of their involvement. A rough pointer to this is provided by the extent to which they
participate in taking decisions. The degree of responsibility and
involvement is exceedingly high, for, in all the types of work function
we have been considering, from half to three-quarters of the mechanical engineers claim to be actively involved in taking decisions connected with their work. Similarly, an American study of scientists
and engineers in six major industrial firms shows that over two-
thirds of the engineers participate (half of them sometimes and half
often) in major decisions affecting their work assignments (Opinion
Research Corp., 1959). While the notion of decision-making is not
likely to be interpreted in an identical manner by all respondents,

nevertheless the high amount of involvement is an indicator of the level at which jobs tend to be held, with equally high participation for the entire range of specialities listed in *Table 18*.

Questions of responsibility will be considered in more detail below, but they must be mentioned at this point in specifying just what it is that the engineer does in his job. Apart from technical tasks, we have seen that there is a considerable amount of office work, administrative work, and decision-taking. The primary question raised by this evidence concerns the extent to which it indicates utilization of professional skill *qua* engineering training. Does one have to be a professional engineer in order to handle the routine clerical work, the administrative tasks, and the simple technical undertakings which take up so much of the engineer's time? Over half of the sample felt that there were aspects of their work that *should* be handled by someone with less training in order to give them the time for more senior work. (The amount of work that *could* be handled by subordinates is likely to be even greater.) The major culprit, cited by over a third of all respondents, was routine clerical work; over a quarter mentioned simple technical work, and almost a fifth referred to administrative work – which in this context is likely to be but a glorified term for clerical office work. The burden of clerical work was felt most keenly among the less successful younger non-graduates and pass graduates with a technical orientation, working in production. An excess of over-simple technical work also tended to be mentioned by the less successful junior staff, particularly in RD and D and in operations, and was felt equally to be a problem for graduates and non-graduates.

An identical question concerning the desirability of shifting routine work to others was utilized in a private survey of technical personnel, which allows comparison of the mechanical engineer with his colleague in other branches of engineering (Social Surveys, Gallup Poll, 1964). It shows that experienced mechanicals, like production engineers, feel more burdened with routine work than do their counterparts in chemical and electronic engineering, and that electrical engineers feel they have even more routine to contend with than do the mechanicals. For those in electronics, the routine work tends to be clerical, whereas for the mechanicals it is more likely to be technical. The problem is a general one in both science and engineering work. For example, an American government survey of attitudes of scientists and engineers reports that more than two-fifths of a sample of scientists and engineers in industry and government said that more than a quarter of their time is spent on duties 'which do not require a technical or specialized knowledge' of their profession (U.S. President's Committee on Engineers & Scientists for Federal Govt Programs, 1957). Important ramifications of this situation are suggested by recent findings which indicate that more highly motivated scientists are less ready than those with low motivation to shift organizational work upon other men (Glaser, 1964).

No description of the engineer's job would be complete without attention to the validity of the most common stereotype of engineering work: to what extent does the engineer in fact wield a greasy spanner? The question concerning the frequency of doing manual work since becoming professionally qualified specified periods of some three days at a time, to rule out more short-lived experiences which would be more frequent. Almost two-thirds of the respondents claim never to have done *any* manual work, a fifth do such work occasionally, and a seventh do some frequently. Frequency of doing manual work is unrelated to variables of age, graduate status, orientation, or success, but, interestingly, those in managerial posts are least likely to admit that they never engage in manual work. Although some two-thirds of all respondents do not indulge in the activity themselves, a majority (57 per cent) feel that it is a good thing to work alongside their men; in contrast, over a third believe that it is *not* advisable to do so in order to maintain status – the latter response being twice as frequent among those who never do manual work.

An item of job description at the opposite extreme from the notion of a greasy spanner and manual toil at the works is the allure of business and professional conferences in far-off places. Three-fifths of the graduates and two-fifths of the non-graduates have travelled abroad in connexion with their work. Such travel is most common among the older, most successful graduates with a good degree, working in managerial and non-industrial settings, and having a knowledge of foreign languages. But it is striking that a fifth of those who travel frequently in connexion with their work and a third of those who do so occasionally do not claim a working knowledge of *any* foreign language. Yet it is unlikely that most travel is to English-speaking nations. [Half of the non-graduates and almost three-quarters of the graduates claim a working knowledge of a foreign language (as compared with 21 per cent of the British public, according to a 1963 Gallup Poll finding). Knowledge of foreign languages is more likely among older engineers, partly owing to their greater need for this skill, but also because they more frequently studied languages in their youth (see Chapter 4). French is the most common language (known by 65 per cent of the graduates and 39 per cent of the non-graduates), and German is second (known by 38 per cent of first-class graduates, 28 per cent of all graduates, and 15 per cent of non-graduates); only 4 per cent of all respondents have Spanish, 3 per cent Italian, and only 10 respondents (1 per cent) Russian; 10 per cent know other tongues.]

AUTHORITY AND COLLEAGUES

The extent of authority which characterizes the engineer's role and some of the major correlates of authority are further aspects of work setting. As has already been indicated, whatever the type of work pursued, at least half of all respondents claim to be actively involved in decision-making in connexion with their speciality, but fewer take other types of decision, such as those about personnel and pur-chasing (on orders of £100 or more).

In all cases it is in the smaller organization that the engineer is more likely to be involved in the wider range of decisions. The smaller organization would appear to confer more status in compensation for its inadequacies in other realms. Of course, it is from positions in management that the major amount of decision-taking originates, with those in operations in second place. Not only is decision-taking a function of particular types of position, it also corresponds to the holding of high-level posts within organizational hierarchies and thus is related to age and success.

The contrasts between those concerned with the engagement of colleagues – qualified engineers – and those involved with the en-gagement of subordinate staff – office and factory personnel – are notable. One-quarter of all respondents take decisions concerning the engagement of colleagues and another quarter claim an advisory role. Thus only half take no part in this process as compared with the two-thirds and three-quarters who take no part in the engagement of office and works personnel. In addition, as might be expected, those who vet their colleagues tend not only to be in higher positions than those who decide on subordinates, but also to be more highly qualified. While graduates and non-graduates take equal responsi-bility among those who engage subordinates, a larger proportion of graduates are involved in decisions concerning the engagement of colleagues. Even more strikingly, while it is the second-class and the pass graduate who are concerned with subordinates, it tends to be the first-class graduate who decides the fate of colleagues.

Decisions concerning large purchases are allocated in a somewhat different manner from personnel decisions in that they correspond to functional specialities rather than to the individual's status in the organization. Only two-fifths of all respondents do not take any part in such decisions.

When decision-taking in connexion with work specialities is combined with decision-taking concerning purchasing and personnel, it is clear that almost all engineers are in decision-making positions. Whatever the speciality or organizational status of an individual, the most common situation is to be involved in decision-making in at least five different areas (the areas being more circumscribed only for those in non-industrial employment). Even among the youngest and most poorly paid segments of the profession, only some 3 per cent admit to having no part either in the taking of decisions or in the discussions on which decisions are based. Indeed, only 10 per cent of the total claim merely an advisory role. Most engineers would appear to be actively involved in the taking of decisions connected with various aspects of their jobs and organizations.

A rather different and perhaps even more revealing indicator of the engineer's status in his organizational hierarchy is his access to a private secretary, whether one working only for the respondent or shared with one or two others. Over half of all the engineers in the sample do have a secretary – a fifth a private secretary and over a third a shared secretary. This asset is much more common in smaller firms and is very much a symbol of success in managerial positions. For example, only 4 per cent of those earning under £1,400 have a secretary of their own in contrast to 70 per cent of those earning £3,000 and over. But a secretary is less clearly a success symbol than a symbol of high managerial status. Four-fifths of those in industrial management have private secretaries as compared with less than half of those in operations, RD and D, or non-industrial posts. To this extent, the secretary serves more as a symbol of the managerial role – perhaps suggesting the degree to which the engineer in this position is removed from the technological function into the realm of administrative office work – than as a symbol of the engineer's status or authority.

Number of subordinates is another indicator of level of responsibility. As with the case of decision-making, it cannot be considered apart from the contexts of functional speciality and organizational type. In the smaller firm, for example, just as there is more decision-taking even by men on the lower echelons, so there is more likelihood of having *some* subordinates, but the total number of subordinates will obviously be limited by the size of the firm. The number of subordinates an individual is in charge of does not vary strongly by type of production process. The total number of subordinates tends, however, to be somewhat greater in process and mass production industries, and least in unit production.

Having no subordinates is a function of both speciality and status. It is most common for those working in RD and D, where almost a third have no subordinates (and two-fifths are in charge of one to ten men). The status significance is seen from the fact that supervisory responsibility is absent among the younger men (under the age of 35), the non-graduate portion of the sample, and the less successful (who are two-and-a-half times as likely as the successful to have no subordinates). The extremes are most strongly shown by income levels. Two-fifths of those earning under £1,400 have no subordinates; the proportion is reduced by half for successive income groups and drops to 1 per cent of those earning £3,000 and over.

Having a hundred or more subordinates tends to occur above the age of 45. It is much more common among graduates than among non-graduates, and is highly related to class of degree – it occurs for 29 per cent of graduates with first-class degrees, 21 per cent of those with seconds and thirds, 15 per cent of pass graduates, and 14 per cent of non-graduates. (Curiously, the supervision of *medium*-sized groups (25–100) is inversely related to class of degree and graduate status.) Supervision of large groups is very much an indicator of success. Only 8 per cent of the less successful have a hundred or more subordinates, whereas among the more successful the proportion is over three times as high. Similarly, over half of those in the top income group have a hundred or more subordinates, the proportion with this number of subordinates being half for the successively lower income groups, and dropping to but 3 per cent of those earning less than £1,400.

For the entire sample, the median number of subordinates is between ten and twenty-four, but the spread is considerable. Thus, one-fifth have no subordinates, one-quarter have between one and nine, one-third between ten and ninety-nine, and one-fifth have a hundred or more. Those whose position is largely managerial are the most prone to be in charge of large numbers. In production, the number of direct subordinates tends to be smaller, and is smallest of all – groups of less than ten – in RD and D work. Though supervision in non-industrial settings tends to involve many separate issues, it may generally be stated that the number of subordinates tends to be small.

To the extent that the engineer is not only an organizational employee, but a professional as well, the depiction of his work situation necessitates attention to colleague as well as authority relationships. More specifically, we are concerned here with the potential for colleague relationships in alternative work situations.

The initial consideration in this context is the total number of qualified engineers or scientists employed at the respondent's place of work. Of course, size and type of industry are the major determinants, with large process industries employing the largest concentrations of qualified technological manpower.

The typical situation for most engineers who, as has been observed, do work for large organizations, is to be numbered among some three or four dozen professional employees. Over a quarter of all respondents – and over a third in the larger firms – work where there are a hundred or more professional technological employees. As has been noted in the discussion of organizational size, younger men are more likely to be found in large firms. Thus they tend to work in settings where there are more professional colleagues. But whereas small and large firms employ similar proportions of graduates and non-graduates, graduates and especially honours graduates are more to be found in establishments employing large aggregates of professional personnel. In such settings there is a larger proportion working in RD and D and operations as opposed to managerial posts, and success is more likely than lack of success. These findings would seem to suggest that sheer size of organization is less revealing than is the level of qualification of those employed.

Working in a setting where there are a large number of professional colleagues suggests certain attributes of the work situation. It also indicates the potential for the development of an occupational community. A more specific indicator of a very similar realm is the number of qualified scientists and engineers worked with directly. The statements that have already been made about the relevance of size and type of industry again apply, the larger working groups being found in large process industries. In the smallest firms, a quarter of the respondents work with no professional colleagues; only half this proportion are in a similar situation in medium-sized firms, and only 5 per cent of those in large firms work in isolation from colleagues.

For the entire sample, a seventh work with no colleagues or with but one other colleague (9 per cent with none), a third work with two to nine colleagues, a fifth with ten to nineteen, and the remaining quarter work in larger groups of twenty or more. The typical situation clearly involves working with a number of colleagues, the median number being about ten.

Working with a large number of colleagues is related to type of speciality, being most frequent in operations and in RD and D. Those in management, of course, tend to have more subordinates than colleagues. Differential qualifications are also reflected in that graduates, and especially those with good degrees, are more likely to work in large colleague groups, of twenty or more, than are pass graduates or non-graduates. Accordingly, this type of work situation tends to be associated with higher income and higher success-rates.

Working *with colleagues* does not necessarily mean that the relationship is one of equality. Clearly, even if all in a working group are professional scientists and engineers, there nevertheless are status levels with superiors and subordinates. The individual's status rating *vis-à-vis* his professional colleagues, for example the seniority of posts in management and non-industrial settings as opposed to those in operations and RD and D, will be analysed in more detail in the next chapter. But an indication of status positions held by those in the sample completes the delineation of the work situation. It is in the small firm that the engineer is most likely to be senior to the colleagues worked with. But, when industrial types are compared, the engineer more frequently holds a senior post in process industries than in unit or small-batch firms. Being in a position of seniority is of course related to age, yet it is significant that over a quarter of those in the youngest age group find a majority of their work colleagues junior to them, suggesting that the engineer begins his organizational career at a fairly high rung on the ladder. Whatever the age, however, graduates much more than non-graduates tend to be in positions of seniority, although their status does not correspond to their class of degree.

HOURS OF WORK

In spite of the dramatic decline in the length of the working week in this century, contemporary man still continues to devote a considerable portion of his total time to work. The details of work schedules thus indicate something about the place of work in total life space (cf. Chapter 9). More specifically, our concern is with the allocation of work within the ranks of the professional mechanical engineers.

The basic number of hours put in each week at the place of work, without overtime, ranges from 36 to 41 hours for two-thirds of the sample. The modal period (for two-fifths of the respondents) is 38 to 39 hours a week, with approximately equal proportions having longer and shorter hours. Additional hours, in evenings and/or at weekends, are not extensive. One-third claim never to work extra hours, for another third extra hours average under six a week, a fifth work seven to twelve extra hours, and a tenth find themselves with twelve hours or more of overtime.

When the basic and extra hours are combined, the average working week – including work taken home – comes to 42 hours. A third work under 40 hours, over a third between 40 and 45 hours, a quarter between 46 and 54 hours, and only 7 per cent 55 hours or more. Compared with his American counterpart, who is twice as likely to work over 55 hours (Wilensky, 1961), the British engineer puts in relatively short hours.

Differences both in respect of organizational setting and in respect of position within the organization help to explain variations in hours of work. As might be expected, it is in the smaller, less bureaucratized firm that long hours (45 and over) are more frequent. It is also in this situation that hours are least regular, making it exceedingly difficult for respondents to estimate averages. Similarly, in non-industrial settings, where there may be some rigid routines but no dictates of the machine, hours tend to be very fluid and frequently long. At the other extreme, in large process industries, where the process regulates the pace, hours are most regular and least likely to exceed the basic schedule.

One type of 'long-hours man' is outside the industrial realm, and is most likely an academic or a consultant. Within industry he is most likely to be in a managerial position, frequently in a small firm. Not only does his position tend to be managerial, but so does his orientation. The man with a technical orientation, the man who works in

RD and D – contrary to what one might expect – very rarely takes his worries home with him. Whether the 'long-hours man' is the industrial manager or the non-industrial type, he tends to be older, as likely as not to be a graduate, and is rewarded for his efforts with a high income.

CHAPTER 6

Career patterns

If the description of work settings in the previous chapter may be considered as the framework within which occupational roles are played, the careers pursued are the centre of the action. Most important in any analysis of careers is the consideration of stages and changes, for movement is the essence of careers. Mobility occurs not only up and down organizational ladders, not only horizontally from one organization to another, but also from one type of work function to another. We shall be concerned with all of these moves, including changes between generations, although emphasizing those that occur as one cohort ages. The most general question concerning careers is, however, that of stages. With what type of position does an engineering career begin and what alternative sequences follow? Is there a typical career pattern? How much movement is there within and between organizations? How much between parts of the country?

FIRST JOBS

The striking contrast between graduates and non-graduates in respect of career pattern, which persists throughout their occupational histories, is apparent with the first job held. As *Table 19*

TABLE 19   First job (other than apprenticeship) by graduate status

Job	Graduates	Non-graduates
	%	%
Workshop	5	21
Draughtsman, designer	23	43
Assistant engineer	42	17
Other jobs (see text)	30	19
Total	100	100

indicates, the first job held by non-graduates, apart from apprenticeship, is usually that of draughtsman or design engineer. In contrast, graduates tend to begin work as 'assistant engineers', a title
that embraces such positions as technical assistant, production
assistant, junior/trainee engineer, or simply 'engineer'. Assistant
engineer posts are more common among second-class graduates than
among either first-class or pass graduates. First-class men slightly
more often than other graduates begin as draughtsmen and are least
likely to begin as managerial trainees. For the second largest group
of non-graduates, a workshop job is the lowest rung of the career
ladder. This type of work, presumably undertaken prior to engineering training, includes such jobs as fitter, turner, machinist, lathe
operator, etc. Respondents held first jobs of other kinds: among the
graduates, 9 per cent began in experimental or research and design
posts and 7 per cent as managerial trainees; of the non-graduates, 7
per cent started in clerical jobs. Still less common first jobs, none of
which accounted for more than 3 per cent of either graduates or non-
graduates, were: inspection, sales, civil service posts, career posts in
the armed forces, and lectureships.

Changes over time are not marked. Younger men, however, are
less likely to have begun in the workshop and tend more frequently
to have started as draughtsmen or in experimental research posts.
Younger non-graduates have increasingly begun their careers as
assistant engineers.

Initial training has greater repercussions upon subsequent career
success than has the nature of the first job held. Whereas graduates
who began in workshop jobs have a 50 per cent chance of attaining
success, non-graduates with similar first jobs face 2 : 1 odds against
success. Similarly, graduates who began as draughtsmen have a
better than even chance of success whereas non-graduates who started
in the drawing office encounter 6 : 4 odds against success. But a
first job as an assistant engineer augurs best for both the graduate
and the non-graduate, resulting in financial success for two-thirds of
the former and half of the latter.

The differential success-rates are partly a function of the contrasting avenues towards which first jobs lead. The graduate who began
as an assistant engineer is as likely to attain a managerial post as one
in engineering operations, while the non-graduate much more frequently terminates on the operations side. Furthermore, beginning
as a draughtsman leads to a post in RD and D (and less chance

of financial success) for the non-graduate more often than for the graduate.

Although present organizational affiliations of graduates and non-graduates are similar (see Chapter 5), their original attachments are not. Non-graduates much more frequently began work in small or medium-sized organizations, apparently coming to larger ones later in their careers. The proportions working for small, medium, and large firms are, however, similar for first jobs and present ones. Though there is a slight tendency for those who began in smaller firms to stay in such units, two-thirds of those who began in small or medium-sized organizations are now working in large ones, and three-quarters of those who began in large organizations remain there.

Commercial and industrial firms are more common as first employers than as current employers, albeit retaining 71 per cent of those who began there. All other types of organization draw men from commerce and industry in subsequent career stages, the only other setting more frequently a first than a subsequent employer being the armed services. The shifts of setting are shown in *Table 20.*

TABLE 20   Shifts in setting of employment

	First job	*Present job*	*% in same type organization*
	%	%	%
Nationalized industry	3	7	50
UK Atomic Energy Authority	–	4	–
Public authority	3	3	19
Commerce & industry	75	64	71
Civil service	5	7	37
University & technical coll.	2	8	12
Armed services	9	2	11
Consulting engineering	2	4	17
Other	1	1	0
Total	100	100	

The first job for three-fifths of the respondents was in the geographical region of their birth. Regions, however, vary considerably in respect of the proportion of native sons that they retain: three-quarters of those born in the North-west, in Northern Ireland, and in the Midlands held their first job there; the proportion dropped to two-thirds for the Northern region, East and West Ridings, and Scotland; to over half for the North Midlands, London and the South-east, and the South-western region; to under half for Wales; and to under one-third for the Eastern and Southern regions.

Not entirely separate from the nature of the first job held is the more general question of the common foundation provided by early work experience, whether as part of apprenticeship or subsequent to it. For mechanical engineers, a critical area of experience is in the drawing office whether the label of the initial job is that of draughtsman or not. Only half of the graduates have had some drawing-office experience as compared with almost three-quarters of the non-graduates. Among the graduates, this type of experience is more common for those with first-class degrees and less common for those with other honours degrees, probably because of the greater connexion of the latter group with non-technical managerial functions. Comparison by age groups shows that there is an increasing trend towards having some drawing-office experience among younger men. The possession of drawing-office experience is highly related to types of career pursued, being of course most common (in 83 per cent of the cases) among those in RD and D, less frequent among those working in operations and management, and least of all among those currently in non-industrial posts. The combined effect of this early experience and the types of career to which it leads is thus seen in a stronger technical than administrative orientation.

CAREER TYPES

The three industrial types we have used throughout this study – management, operations, and RD and D – do not (as we have seen in *Table 17*) correspond to the *details* of work functions. Rather, they may be conceived as major types which, together with the non-industrial category, subsume the alternative constellations of engineering careers. They derive from an analysis of current occupational positions which originally indicated twelve specific work functions, as shown in *Figure 3*.

Most notable is that there are more mechanical engineers in management – some third of the total – than in any other functional

G

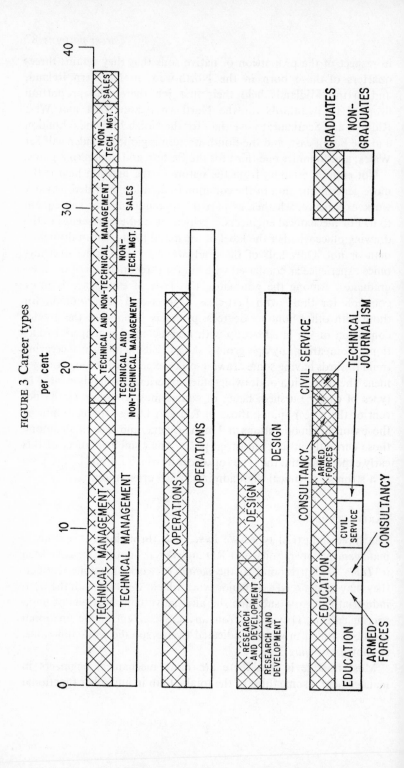

FIGURE 3 Career types

per cent

GRADUATES

NON-
GRADUATES

TECHNICAL MANAGEMENT

TECHNICAL AND NON-TECHNICAL MANAGEMENT

NON-
TECH. MGT.

SALES

TECHNICAL MANAGEMENT

TECHNICAL AND
NON-TECHNICAL MANAGEMENT

NON-
TECH. MGT.

SALES

OPERATIONS

OPERATIONS

RESEARCH
AND DEVELOPMENT

DESIGN

RESEARCH AND DEVELOPMENT

DESIGN

EDUCATION

CONSULTANCY

CIVIL SERVICE

ARMED
FORCES

TECHNICAL JOURNALISM

ARMED
FORCES

EDUCATION

CIVIL SERVICE

CONSULTANCY

CONSULTANCY

category. To expand the conclusions suggested by the analysis of work functions in the previous chapter, this concentration indicates that the 'typical' engineer not only has administrative responsibilities, but *is* a manager, in most cases in a technical management post. To have over a quarter of engineers in operations and production and a mere 7 per cent in research and development raises important questions concerning the uses of manpower commensurate with training. This distribution seems especially anomalous in contrast to American figures, which show only half this proportion in operations and twice as many in research and development (Hawkins, Thoma, & Lebold, 1959). It should be noted, however, that although the American study used similar job categories it is not directly comparable because it is based upon all branches of engineering. Nevertheless, the British concentration in operations suggests undue emphasis upon keeping things going at the expense of innovation and is especially serious in that the proportions employed in research and development have, in recent years, been decreasing (U.S. Department of Commerce, 1963). A comparison of 1962 with 1959 figures shows, on the other hand, a very slight increase (see Advisory Council on Scientific Policy, 1963; cf. Dedijer, 1962).

Except for the marked contrast seen in the fields of design and education, there are not strong differences in the proportions of graduates and non-graduates by career type. The link between university experience and working in the area of education appears obvious. But the absence of graduates among design engineers cannot be so rationally explained. In addition, working in design and operations is negatively associated not only with holding a degree, but also with class of degree held. What graduates there are in these areas are more likely to have a pass than an honours degree, and if an honours degree, it is more likely to be a second or third than a first.

By contrast, positions in management, research and development, and in non-industrial careers – above all in education – are related not only to the possession of a university degree, but even more to the possession of a good honours degree. In management, however, the graduate with a lower-second- or third-class degree is more highly represented (46 per cent of the graduates in these categories) than is the man with a first or an upper-second (39 per cent). It is only in technical management posts that the proportion of first-class graduates is higher; in sales there are no first-class men at all. This preponderance of unassuming seconds over pretentious firsts (which industry tends to deny in attempting to improve its public image) may be due to the predisposition of first-class graduates towards research in either an academic or an industrial setting, but it may also reflect the preference of the large organization for the 'well-rounded' organization man without embarrassing brilliance (see Whyte, 1956). Again, this distribution of manpower raises the question of the appropriateness of the criteria by which talent is allocated.

Changes by age are intrinsic to the very notion of careers. These are shown in *Figure 4.* Apart from a slight tendency for individuals to

FIGURE 4 Career types by age

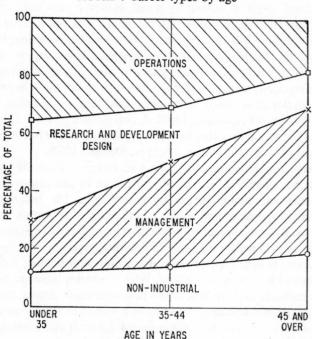

come into non-industrial positions from industrial ones at a later stage in their career, the non-industrial group is relatively stable and what movement there is tends to be internal within this category of careers. The progressive stages of a career may be seen most clearly in the industrial group where, as was noted in the consideration of first jobs, beginning a career in engineering most frequently involves a post of assistant engineer or designer or draughtsman, and thus corresponds to working either in operations or in RD and D.

Most of the early posts described as management were managerial traineeships.

In the second age group (35–44) there is a small decrease in the proportion engaged in operations, but almost a third remain in this sphere. The major change is that the proportion in management has doubled and consists largely of those who have left positions in RD and D. In the third age group, those aged 45 and over, the greatest recruitment continues to be into the ranks of management. However, whereas those who come into management before the age of 45 are mainly from RD and D, those who enter after this age tend to come from positions in operations. Those over 55 show very similar patterns to the 45–54 age group: that is to say, if a man has not succeeded in reaching (nor tried to attain) managerial level by the age of 55, he is unlikely ever to reach it.

The most striking feature of engineering careers in general is that, by the age of 55, half of the profession have attained managerial positions. While this trend is similar for graduates and non-graduates, the former enter the ranks of management at an earlier age. Leaving the area of RD and D with increasing age occurs more among those in research and development than among those in design work, and is more common for graduates than it is for non-graduates. In the non-industrial sphere, recruitment of older age groups is the pattern for careers in education, consultancy, the civil service, and technical journalism; following a technical career in the armed forces is, however, negatively related to age.

Thus the typical career movement of an engineer within industry shows that operations, and, to an even greater extent, research, design, and development, are mainly the work of the younger man. The major direction of movement is into the ranks of management, either early in the career from the RD and D side or, later, from operations.

To the extent that more engineers are employed in management than in any other type of work and that half of the total reach a managerial position by the age of 55, such a post would appear a typical sequel to an engineering career. This interpretation is implicit in such a comment as, 'The engineer who, at forty, can still use a slide rule or a logarithmic table, and make a true drawing, is a failure' (Hughes, 1958, p. 137). But to suggest that all engineers who do not attain managerial positions are failures is clearly a distortion. For, it must be emphasized, half of the profession do *not* become managers, and not all aspire to such posts. In terms of their general work orientation (see Chapter 8), half of all the respondents would prefer a technical position and only a quarter an administrative one, the remaining quarter desiring a combination of both. The lack of identity between actual and desired work is shown in *Table 21*.

TABLE 21   Orientation by career type

Orientation	Career type			
	Management	Operations	RD & D	Non-indus.
	%	%	%	%
Administrative	35	21	12	24
Technical advisory	35	54	62	48
Mixed, technical & administrative	30	25	26	28
Total	100	100	100	100
Number of cases	340	273	217	147

An individual's preference for technical or administrative work will have a considerable influence upon the type of work he pursues. Actual work experience will reinforce attitudes relevant to the particular environment. But, even when career type is used as the independent variable for occupational orientation, disparities remain. For example, among those working as managers, there exists the expected preference for administrative or mixed technical and administrative positions. Yet over a third express a technical preference albeit the work of many is essentially non-technical. This discrepancy is most clear in the case of non-technical managers, one-fifth of whom express a preference for a technical position.

Again, more than half of those in operations and almost two-thirds of those in RD and D would, if the pay were the same, prefer a technical advisory post. But in fact the pay is not the same and, as we have seen, upward mobility with advancing years in most cases necessitates leaving operations or RD and D. Thus although many of the managerial posts open to engineers require technical ability and interest, there would appear to be a considerable amount of reluctant entry into the administrative side attributable to the absence of upper rungs on technical career ladders.

The implications of the various career paths are revealed not only in the differences over age groups but also in the status and rewards that accrue in each. Top positions, as revealed by job titles (e.g. director, head of major division or function, professor, chief scientific officer), are by no means evenly spread over the major career types. Indeed, 70 per cent of those who hold such top positions are in management, and only 15 per cent are in non-industrial careers (9 per cent in operations and 6 per cent in RD and D). Similarly, managerial positions yield the highest incomes, followed by non-industrial posts, operations, and, at the lowest level, RD and D (see Chapter 7 for a fuller discussion of incomes). To a considerable extent this ordering of positions according to income level reflects the age groups to be found in each area; a similar order is obtained, moreover, when the index of success, which combines age and income, is applied.

When success is considered separately for graduates and non-graduates, the findings once again suggest that initial training has greater repercussions than does the career pattern pursued. For, while graduates and non-graduates have been seen to follow relatively similar career patterns, the two groups do not hold identical positions within these patterns, as indicated by the non-graduates' lesser financial rewards. The differential success-rates are shown in *Table 22.*

In all types of careers, graduates have a much better chance of success than have non-graduates. They have greatest success in managerial posts, in a ratio of 3 : 1. In operations and in non-industrial employment graduates also do well, with a success ratio of 3 : 2. They do least well in RD and D, where their chances are just under 1 : 1. The sheer fact of being a graduate gives the individual a 2 : 1 likelihood of achieving the median income for his age group of professional colleagues, and even in the least favoured occupational avenue his chances are almost even.

Non-graduates, on the other hand, are faced with *not* achieving success in 3 out of 5 cases. It is only in managerial positions that they have a better than even chance of success. In the other career patterns, whether operations, RD and D, or non-industrial, in 7 cases out of 10 the median-age income category will not be attained by the non-graduate.

Within the category of management, the type that combines technical and non-technical functions provides the best opportunity

TABLE 22 Success by graduate status by career type

Career type	N	Successful	Unsuccessful	Total
		%	%	%
ALL				
Graduates	387	64	36	100
Non-graduates	590	39	61	100
MANAGEMENT				
Graduates	149	76	24	100
Non-graduates	191	57	43	100
OPERATIONS				
Graduates	97	59	41	100
Non-graduates	176	31	69	100
RD & D				
Graduates	64	47	53	100
Non-graduates	153	30	70	100
NON-INDUSTRIAL				
Graduates	77	60	40	100
Non-graduates	70	29	71	100

for success for both graduates and non-graduates. Within the category of RD and D, those solely concerned with design among both graduates and non-graduates tend to be unsuccessful, while those in research and development have an even chance of success if non-graduates, and a better than even chance if graduates. In the non-industrial category the pattern is for graduates to be successful and non-graduates unsuccessful, with the armed forces and consultancy providing non-graduates with the best chance of attaining success.

MOBILITY

The overall movement from RD and D and operations to managerial positions, given the refinements that have been suggested, outlines the major phases in an engineering career but does not present a detailed picture of the steps involved. For example, the changes of position both within and between organizations show the engineer to have had an average of seven jobs or promotions by the end of his career. Already, by the age of 35, there have been four job moves on average, with one more between the ages of 35 and 44, and two more after 45. The current job has been held for some three years in the youngest age group, for some five years by those aged 35 to 44, and for ten years among the oldest age group. Considering either the number of moves or the length of tenure in the present job, it is clear that job changes are more frequent for the younger man. Graduate and non-graduate patterns are similar, but the former progress more gradually, the non-graduates having experienced as much job movement by the age of 45 as the graduates have at 55. Also, while the oldest group of graduates (55+) have one more move ahead, this is not so for the oldest non-graduates. Managerial posts tend to be the most stable: having reached the top of a ladder, one tends to stay there. To the extent that movement between jobs is in many cases synonymous with promotion, it tends to be associated with success at all ages, but especially in the younger age groups.

Mobility between organizations is, of course, less frequent than movement within the same organization. It is, nevertheless, surprisingly high in comparison with other studies of mobility between industrial firms. Only 16 per cent of the sample have remained with their original employers (18 per cent of the graduates and 14 per cent of the non-graduates). Of the youngest age group, only a quarter have never changed employers, the proportion dropping to a seventh of those between 35 and 44, and to one-tenth of those aged 45 and over. This rate of mobility is higher than that found among managers in industry or among cohorts of graduates in industry in Britain. Clements (1958) found a third of the managers in his study never moved from their first firm. The Acton Society Trust (1956) study of managers reported that 44 per cent started in their current company. Similarly, a study of Cambridge graduates (Craig, 1963) found 44 per cent of those in industry to be with their initial employer ten years after going down.

The average engineer (aged 41) has held his current job for six years, has been with his current employer for 10·2 years of the total of 22·7 years he has been in the labour force, and has worked for 3·36 organizations. Movement between employers is, like job movement, more frequent among younger men, but it is not restricted to younger men. Those under 35 have been with their current employers for six years on average as compared with nine years for those aged 35–44 and sixteen years for those in the oldest age group. Similarly, those under 35 have worked for an average of 2·64 organizations as compared with 3·40 organizations for those aged 35–44 and 4·06 organizations for those aged 45 and over. To the extent that there may have been less movement between firms when the older men began their careers, these figures cannot be predictive of future trends. But, on the basis of these figures, the typical engineer, by the end of his career, will have worked for some four different organizations; two-fifths will have worked for five or more (see *Table 23*).

TABLE 23   Number of different organizations worked for by age

| No. of organizations | Age in years | | |
	Up to 34 (N = 275)	35–44 (N = 442)	45 & over (N = 260)
	%	%	%
1 only	24	14	10
2	32	22	17
3	19	21	17
4	14	18	16
5	7	11	19
6 and more	4	14	21
Total	100	100	100

The average number of organizations worked for is only slightly higher for non-graduates (3·45) than it is for graduates (3·23). Those currently working in non-industrial settings have made the largest number of moves between organizations (4·10), since most posts in consultancy, education, etc., tend to be taken up after initial industrial employment(s). Within industry, those in management have made more moves (3·27) than those in operations (3·22), who, in turn, have moved more than those in RD and D (3·02). However, since differences between these three are small, one can by no means conclude that changing employers frequently is more likely to lead to a post in management. Another factor influencing the likelihood of movement between employers is the size of the organization. Those who began their careers in large organizations will have experienced less movement (3·13) than those in small firms (4·10) since, as we have seen, small firms tend to lose employees to large ones.

While the number of different posts held is associated with success (the successful have held an average of 5·59 and the unsuccessful of 5·26 posts), the number of moves between organizations is negatively associated with success: the successful have on average moved 3·22 times as compared with 3·50 on the part of the unsuccessful. More specifically, success is associated with making up to three moves, while lack of success is associated with moving four times or more before the age of 45. The pattern is especially clear for those respondents who have changed employers six times or more, resulting in success in only 39 per cent of the cases as compared with success for 52 per cent of those who have moved three times or less. Length of tenure with current employer yields a similar finding in that the successful have been longer with their organizations (10·9 years) than the unsuccessful (9·5 years).

Geographical mobility, since it involves uprooting from one section of the country to another, is even less common than movement between employers. Yet, in spite of the prevailing notion that the Englishman is relatively immobile, only one-third of the sample have always worked in one region. Some two-fifths of all engineers are now working in the region of their birth, but since only a third have never changed regions, the proportion is made up by those who left their native area and later returned. The pattern by region for present employment is rather similar to that for first jobs. The areas currently employing about half of their native sons, and no region does better than half, are: North-west and Northern Ireland, Midlands, London and South-east, and Scotland. East and West Ridings employ some two-fifths of their native sons, the figure dropping to one-third for Northern and South-western regions and for Wales, and to one-quarter or less for the North Midlands, Eastern, and Southern regions.

There is more difference between graduates and non-graduates in the extent of their geographical mobility than in the extent of their movement between jobs or organizations. Graduates tend to make more moves between regions (1·99 on average) than non-graduates (1·49). Regional moves have also the characteristic of being spaced throughout the career. By the age of 35, there will have been one move, on average; another will occur between 35 and 44; and a third – for the graduates – after 45. The oldest graduates will have had an average of 2·79 moves as compared with 2·34 for the non-graduates. Those in non-industrial employment have made the largest number of regional moves at all age levels, almost matched by the total number of moves of those in management. It is noteworthy that, above the age of 45, RD and D men have made more geographical shifts than have those in management.

Contrary to the pattern for mobility between organizations, geographical mobility is positively related to success; the successful have made an average of 1·87 regional moves as compared with 1·52 for the unsuccessful. This might appear a contradictory finding in that a geographical move in many cases also involves a change of employer. But it need not mean an organizational shift, since it may refer to a transfer between branches of the same firm. Extent of geographical mobility is, moreover, a more sensitive indicator than is movement between organizations in picking out those who inhibit their opportunities by refusing any move. The effect of a regional move is most noticeable at the extremes: only 38 per cent of those who have made no geographical moves are successful, as compared with 58 per cent of those who have moved five or more times, while those who have moved one to four times have an even chance of success.

The general implications of patterns of mobility for success in engineering careers would appear to be that excessive movement between organizations tends to harm the chances of success; on the other hand, extreme immobility also leads to negative results. The individual unwilling to make at least one geographical move faces considerable odds against achieving success where he is. Moderation in frequency of moves would appear to be the ideal pattern.

The disparity in rates of mobility between engineers and others in industry can be explained by both positive and negative factors connected with the role of the engineer and the facilities of employers. On the positive side, the engineer's professional qualification equips him to use his skill in a variety of settings. He is thus at a decided advantage in the industrial market and is in a position to explore a variety of greener pastures. On the negative side, it may well be that some firms are not able fully to utilize the engineer's abilities or to accord him appropriate rewards, as is suggested by the tendency for greater mobility to occur out of smaller firms.

Expectations concerning future mobility to higher jobs and to other organizations (to be considered in more detail in the next chapter) are shaped by factors similar to those that explain past mobility trends. It is the older man, who has attained a position of seniority in his firm, who is most likely to anticipate future stability in his career. At the other extreme, younger men anticipate change.

While half of the youngest age group think that they *might* attain their highest post with their current employer, only 15 per cent *expect* to remain with their present employer until retirement; the vast majority expressed their expectations about staying where they were in terms of an escape clause: 'it depends upon external circumstances'; or, 'until something better comes up'. The latter response suggests fairly constant scrutiny of the employment advertisements in the Sunday newspapers.

Reasons for changing jobs differ at various stages of the career cycle, the differences being particularly marked as between early and later moves. For both periods of time, however, the two major reasons given are promotion and a better immediate salary, albeit these factors tend to be mentioned more frequently with reference to later moves. External influences, such as being called up for the services or completing a course, account for many early job changes. Frequently, early job moves were undertaken as a means to higher status and salary in the long run and as an opportunity of gaining a broader range of experience. Later moves are even more often explained by such long-range considerations. Whereas successful respondents tend to explain their moves simply in terms of promotions, the less successful appear to rationalize their situation, emphasizing, for example, that they were offered better working conditions, or that they sought a different type of work or a change of firm, or that they were compelled to move owing to the reorganization of the firm, and so on.

An identical question used in a comparative study indicates that a regard for future prospects rather than for immediate salary and status benefits and the desire to move in an administrative direction distinguish mechanical engineers from their colleagues in other engineering branches (Social Surveys, Gallup Poll, 1963).

CHAPTER 7

Attainments, aspirations, and status

Throughout the discussion of background and careers, success – defined by the achievement of the median income for an age group – has been used as a major touchstone. While controlling for age, this measure of success is a relatively crude one, distinguishing only between those who have 'it' and those who do not. Although many fundamental determining factors are revealed by this means, it clearly is not the only way in which attainment can be indicated, nor does it take into account degrees of attainment. For, even on the criterion of financial achievement within an age group, some of the successful are more so than others, as are some of the unsuccessful further below par than others.

Accordingly, this chapter compares alternative criteria of success or attainment, with special attention to its numerical indicator – income. In analysing income and other measures of attainment we are not assuming that virtue or skill or any particular quality is rewarded. Indeed, as fiction tends to emphasize, success itself is often less than rewarding (Rillie, 1964). But, given that income is obviously a reward, our concern is with the question of what factors *are* rewarded.

Beyond current attainments, which can be assessed, lie hopes for the future – the realm of aspirations. These, in the context of our investigation, relate mainly to the individual's career plans, but the wider aspect is taken into account in noting his plans for his children. Another view of attainment – in addition to what the individual has himself accomplished or hopes to achieve, or what he would like to pass on to his progeny – considers the status of the engineering profession itself.

ATTAINMENT

When success was measured in terms of the attainment of the median income for an age group, the determining influences that were examined included those of background, training, and career. The effects of various background factors were seen to be highly inter-related, with the possession of a good degree from a university emerging as more significant than family background or type of school attended. The major contrast between graduates and non-graduates remained a more fundamental criterion than type of industry or organization worked in, the chances for success afforded by most work settings being similar. The managerial ladder was the most likely upward path and a moderate amount of mobility between organizations enhanced the chances for success.

Job title
Alternative indicators of career attainment, which tend to be more restrictive in bestowing the label of success, nevertheless reveal similar patterns. Using the basic measure of success, we have arbitrarily considered half of the respondents successful. Considerably fewer are successful, however, if one analyses job titles – which, in spite of the variety of systems of organization in which engineers work, can be classified in three gross levels: 'top people' (i.e. director; head of major division or function, e.g. works manager, chief engineer; professor; chief scientific officer; technical editor); middle-level positions (e.g. engineer, technician, lecturer); and clearly low-status positions (e.g. draughtsman). Less than a third of all respondents emerge as clearly high status by this criterion, with the vast majority (three-fifths) in the middle category, and only the remaining few in the low category.

Although some ambiguity is engendered because the status significance of the same title can vary from one firm to another – and because there is the practice of using a higher job label as a reward in itself, unaccompanied by a commensurate salary increase – attainment in terms of job titles does broadly correspond to our original success measure. Seven-tenths of those with high-status job labels are classified as successful, but so are four-tenths of those whose titles are not in this category. Reference has already been made (Chapter 6) to the overwhelming preponderance of high-sounding labels in the managerial sphere as contrasted with RD and D, operations, and non-industrial settings. At the other extreme, most of the clearly low-status jobs are in RD and D, mainly the job of draughtsman. The basic difference between graduates and non-graduates appears again in that 44 per cent of the former are top people as indicated by the title on their office doors, as compared with but 26 per cent of the latter. Of the graduates, some half of the honours-degree recipients are in high-status jobs, class of honours degree having little effect, whereas only 37 per cent of pass-degree men are in comparably high posts. The greatest amount of designatory status is received by Camford graduates (52 per cent), with London second (47 per cent), and provincial graduates last (40 per cent). Attainment of a high-status job is of course highly related to age, being found in only 12 per cent of those under 35, and in 31 per cent of those aged 35–44, 53 per cent of the 45–54 age group, and 69 per cent of those aged 55 and over.

Future career goals

A more stringent measure of attainment than job label is the subjective feeling on the part of the respondent that he has already achieved the top of his profession. This was ascertained indirectly by asking the individual about his plans and goals for his future career. Again, the correlates of 'having arrived' are similar to those indicated by other measures of attainment, albeit only 12 per cent of the sample volunteered that they were already at the top. Over three-quarters of these have high-status job titles and some two-thirds are successful on the basis of the age-income measure. These self-defined *arrivistes*, who are as likely to be in non-industrial posts as in management, included only a slightly higher proportion of graduates (16 per cent) as compared with non-graduates (11 per cent), but the graduates tended to be those with first-class degrees (22 per cent vs. 13 per cent of those with other honours degrees or a pass degree). As would be anticipated, virtually no one below the age of 35 was presumptuous enough to claim that he had reached the peak of his career. Even the 'crown princes' in family firms would express plans for development. Of those in the second age group (35–44) only 7 per cent felt themselves to have attained their top position, the proportion rising to 19 per cent of those aged 45–54; even among those aged 55 and over, only 53 per cent did not aim further.

Income

Income is in many respects the clearest indicator of attainment. It is one of the most fundamental 'facts of life' of the world of work and, no doubt for this reason, there exists some information for other occupational groups which allows the mechanical engineers to be put into perspective. Comparison with other professions is not easy since the available data have frequently been compiled on different bases and because the effects of seniority, as shown by career income curves, differ greatly from one profession to another. The most general statement that might be made is that engineers are among the top 6 per cent of all income-earners in Britain – over £1,500 per annum. They are approximately on the level of a senior executive officer in the civil service, or on a par with the typical ranges of income of professions such as those of architect or university lecturer; they rank above teachers, and below solicitors and doctors in general practice (see *The Financial Times*, 18 December 1963, and *The Economist*, 30 May 1964.) The obvious comparison to be made is that between various branches of engineering; for this purpose detailed information is obtainable from the Engineers' Guild surveys on the incomes of professional engineers for 1959–60 and 1962–63, which, in addition to mechanical engineers, cover civil, electrical, and chemical engineers (Engineers' Guild, 1961, 1964*b*).

These surveys show that in *all* branches of engineering, at all age levels, graduates earn more than non-graduates. In the 1959–60 survey both graduate and non-graduate mechanical engineers had higher median incomes than had similar groups among civil and electrical engineers, but they had lower median incomes as compared with chemical engineers. In the United States, incomes follow the same order from high to low: chemical, mechanical, electrical, and civil (National Society of Professional Engineers, 1956). Because of the higher proportion of non-graduates among the mechanicals in Britain, however, the total median income for the profession was lower than that in electrical engineering. The 1962–63 survey shows a marked levelling-up of the differences between incomes of members of the four institutions. While graduate mechanicals remain second only to graduate chemicals, non-graduate mechanicals emerge behind non-graduates of the other three institutions. As a result, the total median income of mechanicals also drops to fourth place. But the levelling trend would appear to be of greater significance than the changes in rank order.

Table 24 summarizes our findings on income. It specifies in detail many of the general patterns we have subsumed in the discussion of factors associated with success in the preceding chapters. The fundamental distinction, whether one considers upper or lower quartiles or the median figure, is between graduates and non-graduates. The consequences of category of university attended and of class of degree

TABLE 24   Income

	Lower quartile	Median quartile	Upper quartile	Number of cases
	£ p.a.	£ p.a.	£ p.a.	
GRADUATES				
Under 35	968	1,215	1,961	95
35–44	1,672	2,164	2,905	179
45 & over	1,915	2,513	3,404	113
NON-GRADUATES				
Under 35	750	825	1,014	180
35–44	1,215	1,576	2,190	263
45 & over	1,594	2,089	2,859	147
ALL GRADUATES	1,502	1,979	2,742	387
ALL NON-GRADUATES	1,134	1,470	2,069	590
CAREER TYPES				
Non-industrial	1,306	1,701	2,354	147
Management	1,602	2,115	2,919	340
Operations	1,115	1,440	2,020	273
RD and D	988	1,240	1,711	217
R and D	1,149	1,490	2,091	68
Design	903	1,091	1,453	149
CLASS OF DEGREE				
Firsts	1,596	2,109	2,915	113
Other honours	1,500	1,998	2,807	126
Pass	1,305	1,726	2,442	148
UNIVERSITY				
London	1,515	1,993	2,750	134
Camford	1,710	2,260	3,109	63
Provincial	1,425	1,873	2,597	179
All External	1,385	1,814	2,512	72
Internal	1,521	2,007	2,783	270

These figures are based upon the analysis of responses in four income categories and have been computed on the basis of a lognormal distribution (cf. Aitchison & Brown, 1957, Chapter 11).

attained (as discussed in Chapter 4) are also clearly reflected. In figures related to career types (see Chapter 6) graduates and non-graduates have been combined. Special attention should be given to the differences in income earned in research and development as opposed to design, since these have been combined in much of our discussion: while the former yields incomes on a par with those received by all non-graduates, design pays even less.

The combined effects of graduate status and age upon income received are shown in another way in *Table 25*, which also reveals the spread of incomes underlying the success measure. For the first

TABLE 25   Graduate status, age, and income

Income p.a.	Graduates by age			Non-graduates by age		
	-35	*35–44*	*45+*	*-35*	*35–44*	*45+*
	%	%	%	%	%	%
–£1,400	53	5	6	79	28	12
£1,400–£1,799	28	30	14	17	39	25
£1,800–£2,999	16	52	40	4	27	46
£3,000+	3	12	40	–	6	17
	100	100	100	100	100	100
No. of cases	95	179	113	180	263	147

age group, for whom £1,200 is the criterion of success, there is a much narrower spread of incomes for the non-graduates, four-fifths of whom are in the lowest income category. For the middle age group the dividing line for success is £1,800: whereas almost two-thirds of the graduates are above this line, an even larger proportion of non-graduates are below it. Among those aged 45 and over, where success is defined as the middle of the third income category, at £2,200, more non-graduates are to be found in this income category than in any other, but the graduates are as likely to be in the top bracket as they are to be in the third one. Thus, for graduates, it is typical to progress from the first income category to the third, and either stay there or go on to the highest. Non-graduates likewise begin in the first category, but then proceed only to the second, and finally to the third, very few going further. These trends may also be seen in the figures presented in *Table 24*.

The influence of type of work done by graduates and non-graduates upon the income received is shown in *Table 26*. Not only do

TABLE 26   Career type, graduate status, and income

Income p.a.	Management Grad.	Non-grad.	Operations Grad.	Non-grad.	RD & D Grad.	Non-grad.	Non-industrial Grad.	Non-grad.
	%	%	%	%	%	%	%	%
−£1,400	8	19	22	49	35	58	17	29
£1,400–£1,799	15	25	30	33	31	23	32	43
£1,800–£2,999	45	40	38	15	31	18	40	24
£3,000+	32	16	10	3	3	1	11	4
	100	100	100	100	100	100	100	100
No. of cases	149	191	97	176	64	153	77	70

income levels correspond to career type, but in each area graduates and non-graduates fare quite differently, the latter being in almost every instance represented much more frequently in the two lower income categories. In operations, graduates cluster in the third income category, but non-graduates are concentrated in the first. In non-industrial posts, graduates tend again to be in the third income category, whereas non-graduates are in the second. In RD and D graduates are almost evenly spread over the first three income categories, while non-graduates cluster heavily in the first. Hardly anyone attains the highest income range in RD and D, whether graduate or not. The non-graduates do less well than the graduates in management also, but clearly have their best chance of attaining the third income category there (see Chapter 6).

EXPECTATIONS AND ASPIRATIONS

In looking beyond what has been attained to speculations about the future, it might be useful to distinguish between aspirations and expectations, between what one would like to achieve and what is realistically anticipated. Though the distinction is not an easy one to make, most answers to items in this area suggest a fairly firm grounding in the realities of the occupational world rather than conjecture about an ideal.

Realistic possibilities

An awareness of actual possibilities is shown in the guesses that respondents made concerning the highest income they expected to earn in any one year of their lifetime, in terms of current values. Although expectations tend to be inflated in comparison with actual attainments, they reflect the correlates of attainment to a high extent. The level of expectation would appear to be a function of both actual achievement and possibilities within particular career lines. Thus, younger men are more modest in their expectations than are their elders. The youngest group (under 35) are almost evenly divided between those who do not envisage ever receiving more than £2,200, those who anticipate a maximum of £3,000, and those who expect to exceed £3,000. By contrast, the most common expectation of older men (given by two-fifths of those over 35) is for an income in the £3,000–£6,000 range. Great expectations are highly related to success already attained: seven-tenths of the successful expect to exceed £3,000, and the same proportion of the unsuccessful never expect to attain this amount.

Graduates and non-graduates appear to be well aware of the differential opportunities available to them, as shown in *Table 27*.

TABLE 27   Highest annual income expected in lifetime by graduate status and career type

Income p.a.	Grad.	Non-grad.	Mgmt.	Op.	RD & D	Non-indus.
	%	%	%	%	%	%
Under £2,200	9	29	10	24	35	20
£2,200–£2,999	23	31	18	33	33	35
£3,000–£3,999	50	31	26	24	21	27
£4,000–£5,999			22	12	6	10
£6,000 +	13	5	17	4	3	5
Don't know	5	4	7	3	2	3

Three-fifths of the non-graduates do not anticipate reaching £3,000, whereas an even larger proportion of the graduates expect to surpass this amount. Non-graduates are equally spread over the three lower categories of expectation but graduates cluster in the more affluent upper regions. The comparison of actual income (*Table 25*) and expected income (*Table 27*) shows the extent to which both groups are unrealistic in their expectations. Only 17 per cent of the oldest non-graduates earn £3,000 and over, yet double this proportion of all non-graduates expect to attain this amount before their careers are over. Similarly, 40 per cent of the oldest graduates earn £3,000 and over, but 63 per cent of all graduates expect to do so.

Table 27 shows in addition the influence of career type on income expectations. Those in RD and D are – realistically – the least hopeful of surpassing £3,000 and the most resigned to remaining below £2,000. This attitude may reflect either an awareness of available possibilities or the lesser concern with financial goals of the head-in-clouds researcher. Those working in management have the highest expectations, some two-thirds looking forward to at least £3,000, and as many as two-fifths anticipating surpassing £4,000. Those in operations and in non-industrial posts resemble each other very closely in what they see ahead, falling between the extremes represented by management and RD and D. In all types of career a much higher proportion expect to attain the higher income brackets than is warranted by current distributions, as an examination of *Table 26* reveals.

Exaggerations concerning future incomes are only to be expected. Indeed, one might emphasize the restraint indicated by the range of responses. The small proportions answering 'don't know' are also notable – given the speculative nature of the question. They suggest that long-range salary conjectures are not far removed from current thinking; people think about money.

Organizational ladders

More abstract plans or goals for one's future career – expressing general aspirations rather than specific expectations – are less readily formulated. As many as 17 per cent of all respondents can state no plans or goals for their future careers, while 12 per cent feel that whatever aims they had in the past have already been realized in that they are already at the top of their profession.

Almost half of all responses concerning aspirations were made in terms of attaining particular levels of organizational hierarchies, whether in industry, education, or the civil service. A much less frequently occurring response involved reference to general personal ambition apart from specific rungs on organizational ladders, e.g. to advance as far as possible, to get ahead, to take advantage of opportunities as they arise, etc. Other themes, none of which was mentioned by more than 3 per cent of the sample, included: non-career technical and scientific goals in research, concern with the prosperity of the organization, the desire to do work in consultancy, to have one's own business, and to accumulate a large amount of money. There were scattered references to leaving engineering entirely and to retirement.

That the only pervading theme referred to steps on organizational ladders is, however, the main point. It is most revealing of the perspective of the engineer, the perspective of the organization man; in the expression of their aspirations, there are no substantial differences between graduates and non-graduates.

Being more specific about future goals requires attention to placement in the organizational hierarchy. When those who have already achieved their desired summit are combined with those who are still loooking forward to it, a generally high level of aspiration is revealed, consistent with the high income expectations. Over half of the sample have attained or expect to reach a high post, in senior management – mainly on the technical side – or in top academic or civil service ranks, or in consultancy. Less than a third restrict their expectations to middle-level positions, while the remainder find themselves unable to answer a question of this type. Clearly, the distinction is between aspirations for top- and middle-ranking posts; although non-graduates are more modest than graduates, the difference between graduate and non-graduate levels of expectation is not so marked as in the case of income hopes. The non-graduates are more likely to define their maximum attainment in terms of a middle-level position and, if aiming for the top, to anticipate a managerial post with a specifically technical content, while the top managerial posts to which the graduates aspire are more likely to be non-technical. Those who have already set foot on managerial ladders are the most likely to be aiming for the top. Men in operations are more oriented towards positions in top management – especially technical posts – than are those in RD and D whose aim is mainly upon middle-level positions.

Mobility
Anticipation of movement upward by no means necessarily includes movement outward to another organization. Even among the youngest age group, half believe that they might attain their top position with their present employer, the proportion not anticipating

a move to a different employer rising to 70 per cent of those aged 35–54 and to 85 per cent of those aged 55 and over.

But although so many think they *might* rise with their present employer, the numbers who *expect* to stay where they are until retirement are much smaller. Those most inclined to move, or at least to be on the lookout for better opportunities, tend to be the young and less successful, and to be employed in operations or RD and D; those in non-industrial posts are more mobile in inclination than those on managerial hierarchies. The commitment to stay on until retirement is related to the expectation of high future income. It is most frequent among those in the most obviously bureaucratic careers in the civil service and the armed forces. Curiously, however, those in educational institutions appear the least stable in their expectations of tenure, being inclined to anticipate moves either to other institutions or out of education entirely.

Aspirations for children

Career contingencies, to the extent that they determine income, are the foundation of other types of aspirations that an individual has. Own career apart, the set of aspirations that is probably of the greatest immediate concern to most people relates to the education and eventual occupation of their children. The desire to have a son (and perhaps even a daughter) become an engineer is also a personal career factor, in its extension of the career beyond the self. More generally, the types of schools to which engineers send their children suggest something of their extra-occupational aspirations and values.

Our findings in this area involve a combination of actual attainments – for those respondents whose children are already at school, university, or work – and aspirations – for those with younger children. Half the respondents have children aged 5 and over, a quarter have children aged 14 and over.

Types of schools planned or attended are similar for sons and daughters. The type of school to which children are sent is highly related to the graduate status of the father, suggesting a distinction between upper-middle- and middle-class patterns. A quarter of the graduates have (or will have) children in public schools as compared with 14 per cent of the non-graduates, the proportions being reversed for secondary, grammar, and comprehensive schools. The graduates with honours – especially first-class – degrees are, interestingly, most prone to send their children to public schools. Income, however, is an even greater determinant of public-school expenditure than is father's educational background. Of those with children aged 5 or over, three-quarters in the top income group (£3,000+) choose public schools for their offspring, the proportions for descending income groups dropping to 32, 17, and 12 per cent. Similarly, over two-fifths of the successful opt for public schools as compared with less than half this proportion of the unsuccessful. Father's occupational status is equally influential: three-quarters of the managers with children aged 5 or over, many of whom had themselves been to public schools, favour similar institutions for their progeny, but in all the other career types the proportion is one-quarter or less.

University attendance, which is, of course, much less likely for daughters than for sons, follows a similar pattern since it tends to be related to attendance at public schools. But on this point the educational background of the father and his occupational status are more significant than his income. Unlike public-school education, university education need not be financed by the parents, unless they fail the means test. What parents do provide is the motivation to attend university. Thus, of the graduates with boys aged 14 or over, two-thirds have sons already following in their footsteps or expect them to do so. This pattern is related to the father's class of degree. A similar desire for university education for their sons is found in only 37 per cent of the non-graduate fathers. Camford graduates are most likely to expect their sons to follow in their footsteps, to university at least, if not to Camford. Provincial graduates, in turn, have higher university expectations for their sons than have London graduates. Father's success is unrelated to the university pattern for sons; income is related (half of the top income group compared with a third of the lowest income group opt for university for their sons), but the association is weaker than that found for graduate or non-graduate status. Unlike the desire for public-school education, university expectations for children are stronger among those employed in non-industrial posts than among managers, and are less likely among those in operations than among those in RD and D.

Almost a quarter of those who have sons expect them to become engineers, an impressive rate of occupational inheritance in view of the fact that only 4 per cent of the sample were themselves the sons of engineers. Passing on the vocation is somewhat more likely on the part of non-graduates than it is among graduates (26 per cent and 20 per cent respectively). It is, in any case, the successful man, especially if in a managerial position, who is most likely to find his footsteps being followed – or to have induced succession. Other professions draw most of the sons, the appeal of allied fields like architecture or pure science being less strong than that of engineering itself. The field of industry – without prior professional qualifications – is also less popular than engineering. The number who do not know what occupations their sons will pursue is large (half of those with sons under 14, a fifth of those with sons between 14 and 18). Accordingly, the proportion whose sons eventually become engineers may be greater than a quarter.

STATUS

Whatever an individual's attainments or aspirations within the ranks of the engineering profession, he tends to be attributed a similar standing to others in the field when viewed by the outsider. For better or for worse, all are engineers. As far as the majority of engineers are concerned, the judgement is for the worse, because the status of their profession is not felt to be high (cf. Strauss & Rainwater, 1962, especially Chapter 9). Less than a third of the engineers claim satisfaction with the status they are accorded in Britain today, and over half voice specific frustrations and dissatisfactions. Not all feel equally badly treated, however, depending upon their standing *within* the profession. Thus the older, more successful graduates in managerial posts express least dissatisfaction – although honours graduates are less satisfied than non-graduates. But, regardless of the degree of personal achievement or success, regardless of occupational setting or type of career, the majority of engineers are dissatisfied with the status of their profession.

Colleagues' evaluations

Evaluation of status requires attention to the question of who bestows it. The most immediate referents are clearly the work situation and the attitudes of non-engineering colleagues. Since engineers claim that theirs is a decidedly under-evaluated occupation, it is surprising that as many as one-quarter profess not to know how their non-engineering colleagues feel towards them. Another quarter state that their colleagues' attitude is neutral or, at best, they qualify it, e.g.: 'They do not understand what the job of the engineer is'. Thus they feel unloved because their colleagues do not understand them – a problem not unique to the world of work. Only a third give their colleagues' attitude as clearly favourable, and one-fifth feel it to be unfavourable. Favourable evaluations were mostly expressed in terms of the respect the job or profession is accorded, being most frequently mentioned by older men – who receive more deference – and by non-graduates rather than graduates, the latter having higher status reference points, resulting in unfulfilled higher expectations. Attainment of success has no influence at all on the perception of favourable-unfavourable evaluations, which is, again, only slightly associated with career type. Consultants stand out in agreeing that they tend to be highly regarded, which is consistent with their occupational role. At the other extreme are the academics, whose colleagues apparently make them feel below both the other cultures in the senior common room.

Those who felt that the attitude of their colleagues was unfavourable talked in terms of being underestimated and looked down upon, their educational attainments and technical skills not being sufficiently recognized. A less frequently occurring explanation played on the theme of dirt and overalls, the engineer as 'a hairy man dieting off axle grease and beer' (*New Society*, 1 August 1963, p. 5), undifferentiated from a garage mechanic. In an attempt to elicit the nature of the abuse engineers feel themselves subject to, respondents were asked what kinds of snide or nasty remarks their colleagues might make about them in banter. Contrary to prevailing stereotypes, and possibly partly in defence against such stereotypes, almost two-thirds (63 per cent) denied having heard any snide remarks. Denials are voiced equally by graduates and non-graduates, and by men at the top and at the bottom of organizational hierarchies, but they are most frequently made by those employed in RD and D and least often by those in operations. It is probable that this last finding reflects differential exposure and not differential perception, since those in operations come closest to what is 'really' engineering work, have to work with a wider range of individuals, and thus are most subject to any abuse that is aroused; those in RD and D, on the other hand, may frequently pass as scientists rather than technologists.

The rhetoric of snide comments is extensive and perhaps most revealing in the absence of any one stereotype. The most frequent theme was that of nuts and bolts: the engineer as a spanner basher, a propeller polisher, a plumber, an oil squirter, a rude mechanical wielding a screwdriver. Not entirely separate from this emphasis upon the use of tools is the notion of doing dirty, manual work: hewers of wood and drawers of water, oil-stained chaps with greasy overalls. Laziness is also frequently mentioned: an easy job, sitting down all day, a major part of the time spent in drinking tea. The comments about laziness do not suggest anything intrinsic to the engineers' occupational role except when accusing him of *not* getting sufficiently dirty. On the economic side, there are some references to salary, for instance to underworked, overpaid, and bloated plutocrats. Comments about the economics of production were even more frequently voiced: the products made are too expensive; engineers are robbers, they are not worth their keep. Finally, there is the notion of the boffin, the egghead, or the slide-rule wizard, and, at the other extreme, that of the low-brow type, without culture, ungentlemanly, with too narrow a view. Awareness of the source of the banter, as coming from subordinates or from actual colleagues and superiors, reconciles some of the seeming contradictions. Whereas equals may scoff at the engineer's occasional dirt, subordinates take greater note of the fact that there is usually no dirt. Similarly, whereas subordinates would make the notion of egghead seem derogatory, status equals would achieve this effect with the appellation of low-brow.

Place in occupational hierarchy
A major indicator of status in the broader community is provided by an analysis of occupational rankings involving that sector of the occupational hierarchy which the engineer is likely to make his point of reference (Gerstl & Cohen, 1964). Given the nature of the engineering profession – one whose members are both professionals and employees – there are two relevant contexts. It was the aim, therefore, to select, for each frame of reference, occupations which, to the engineer, would appear higher than, equal to, or lower than, his own. First, there is the world of the established professions to which, by most criteria of professionalism, the engineer belongs, albeit with a degree of ambiguity. Doctors and solicitors are the obvious established professions. Dentists are also included in this analysis, for, though they are a 'free profession', their status is less clear and they appear likely bait for downgrading by status-seeking occupational groups. The second context is that of the corporate hierarchy. It is his employment – as an employee – that most confounds the professional standing of the engineer. Clearly, at the top of this hier-

archy is the company director. Competing with the engineer for status claims are other professionals working in a similar context, including the research physicist – representing the general realm of science – and the chartered accountant. In a lower position on the corporate pecking-order, without professional qualifications, is the works manager.

Since engineering, in addition to being a profession and a form of industrial employment, is also, on the research side, a science, and even in application is science-based, the research physicist may be viewed as a rival for status claims in both the corporate and the scientific social systems. Closely related to the scientific aspect is the academic sphere, and the occupation of university lecturer, like that of company director, provides not only a point of comparison for the engineer but a possible aspiration (or achievement) as well. Finally, the tenth occupation selected was that of school teacher which, although in the academic realm, was used not for this reason but rather to represent an additional low-status profession.

The occupations ranked all come from the high-prestige sector of the occupational hierarchy. They embrace professions, industrial occupations, and professionals employed in industry. The ten were ranked by the engineers themselves and by the general public. Both the engineers and a national quota sample were asked: 'Would you rank each of the occupations on this card on the basis of how much

TABLE 28   Rankings of occupation by national sample and by engineers

National sample (*N = 1,063*)	*Median rank*	*Engineers* (*N = 977*)	*Median rank*
1. Doctor	2·21	1. Doctor	2·22
2. Solicitor	4·25	2. Company director	2·75
3. University lecturer	4·36	3. Solicitor	3·86
4. Research physicist	4·62	4. University lecturer	4·28
5. Company director	4·65	5. Professional engineer	5·22
6. Dentist	5·96	6. Chartered accountant	5·72
7. Chartered accountant	6·45	7. Research physicist	5·96
8. Professional engineer	7·07	8. Dentist	6·73
9. Primary school		9. Works manager	6·99
teacher	7·67	10. Primary school	
10. Works manager	8·27	teacher	9·78

social prestige you personally feel these occupations have?' The order of ranking according to the national sample is presented on the left side of *Table 28*. Although all the ten selected occupations would be generally regarded as having high prestige, the emergent order suggests discriminations that are less evident in longer, more varied, lists: the established professions and the academic-scientific ones rank above the representative of the top of the corporate hierarchy; the dentist lacks the mystique of the medical world; and the professional employees come even lower. The engineer, as far as the public is concerned, is found quite near the bottom of the list, with only the primary school teacher among professionals and the works manager among corporate employees ranking lower.

Subjective ranking

Whereas the public tends to downgrade the industrial occupations, especially the professional engineer, the engineers themselves (as shown on the right side of *Table 28*) produce a contrasting pattern, upgrading not only their own profession but those related to it as well. Though one-step changes could be due to chance, the overall pattern is unmistakable: the four occupations elevated by the engineer – his own, and those of director, accountant, and works manager – are all from the corporate situs. The only demotion in this realm, that of the physicist, probably reflects direct status and job competition. Thus the engineer not only behaves like the member of any other occupation in overestimating his own status, but carries his colleagues up with him, suggesting that he considers the entire industrial realm his reference group.

In addition to agreeing in assigning a high rank to their own occupation, the engineers show more consensus concerning their high rank than the public does about their low one (a quartile deviation of 1·77 vs. 1·93). The correlates of assigning high rank to their own occupation, although indicating some explanatory factors based upon differences among engineers, tend on the whole to substantiate the degree of their occupational consensus. The similarities in the engineers' responses are more impressive than their differences. University graduates and older men tend to assign themselves higher status, but status evaluation is more strongly influenced by work orientation than by objective conditions of work such as income or job setting. Those most highly committed to their profession ranked it most highly.

Although three-fifths of the engineers give their occupation a high rating – among the top six – less than a third can specify consistent reasons for this evaluation. The most common explanations are: engineering is an important job; it *has* the same status as other professions; engineers are well educated and have a long training; they carry a great deal of responsibility; the prosperity of the firm, of the country, depends on engineers; and, engineers are not rated highly enough. A tone of defensiveness seems to pervade many of these responses.

On the negative side, the most frequent explanation for giving a low ranking is the feeling that the engineer *has* low status. In addition, the ambiguity of the engineering role appears highly salient, as indicated by references to the variety of job levels, the many types of engineer, and the misleading usage of the term 'engineer', which is applied to mechanics as well as to professionals. Other negative factors are felt to be employee status and the limited responsibility of the engineer.

Over a third of the engineers thought that the general public would rank the ten occupations in the same way that they themselves did. Of those who felt that there would be a discrepancy, most recognized that engineers would receive a lower rating by the public. Indeed, when the engineers rank the occupations as they think the public would, their profession emerges even lower than it actually is evaluated by the national sample – ninth, followed only by school teachers. Thus, in this second estimate, the engineering occupation is restored to its 'rightful' low place, indicating that the engineers in their own rankings gave themselves a high status which they know they are not accorded by the public.

Professional commitment

Commitment in this context means the extent of the individual's dedication to and involvement in his work. For its evaluation, therefore, it is necessary to delineate the nature of work involvement in the engineering profession, to which only indirect reference has been made in discussing work settings, career types, and motives for job mobility. The fundamental question is: What does working in engineering mean to an individual? What are the relevant themes? What are the sources of pleasure and discontent? To what extent is the engineer's commitment in fact to his profession – as evidenced by research publications and participation in other institution activities – and to what extent is it oriented towards his place of employment? Does the perspective of the organization man overshadow that of the professional? Are the two allegiances compatible? Similarly, what is the extent of concern with technical problems and technical career lines rather than with managerial ones? Another aspect of commitment is that of intensity: how does the engineer compare with other occupational groups in how much his work means to him? How important is his work in relation to other facets of daily life? Does there tend to be a fusion or segregation of work and the rest of life, as shown, for example, in whether colleagues are included among intimate friends?

COMMITMENT TO WHAT?

A fundamental starting-point in the analysis of the meaning of work is whether the task performed is regarded only as a means to an end – an uninteresting or distasteful occupation tolerated by the alienated worker for the income it yields or for want of any alternative – or as a pursuit which is in itself rewarding. At the upper end of the occupational hierarchy, certainly in the professions, work tends to provide intrinsic rewards as well as extrinsic ones (see, for example, Morse & Weiss, 1955; Fogarty, 1964; Wilensky, 1964b). But the question still remains whether the primary orientation is towards the task performed, or towards activities associated with the work, such as human relations. Neither the basic motivation nor the ideology relevant to a profession is invariably obvious or derivable from the work function performed. For example, while humanitarian themes are likely to predominate in medical ideology (and, it is hoped, in the motivation of medical personnel as well), when the job of work is less glorified by society, as for example dentistry, the members of the occupation tend to express their major source of satisfaction in terms like 'dealing with people' (Gerstl, 1961*a*). Perhaps it is because, in contemporary society, even the most simple machine is potentially more interesting than a mouthful of teeth that the engineer, in contrast to the dentist, so readily admits 'workmanship' as his major source of satisfaction (cf. Becker & Carper, 1956).

Satisfaction in craftsmanship

When engineers state the types of satisfaction they derive from their work, the theme of craftsmanship clearly predominates, in over two-thirds of the replies. It tends to be expressed in such terms as: 'seeing a job completed and working', 'creative satisfaction', 'seeing the tangible results of my designs', 'solving problems', 'maintaining efficient production', 'producing original ideas', and 'accuracy and quality'. Among responses subsumed by the notion of workmanship, creative satisfaction and seeing the end-product were most frequently mentioned. Smaller numbers were specifically concerned with their scientific contribution to the field of engineering, to efficiency in terms of cost or time, and with their public service. Responses not emphasizing the craft of engineering tended to be made in terms of organizational allegiances and to refer more generally to human relations. They included concern with the growth or prosperity of the firm, and satisfactions derived from exercising authority and initiative, from teamwork, and from having a wide range of personal contacts. In addition, there was reference, mainly on the part of teachers, to satisfaction from imparting knowledge and shaping careers. Only 4 per cent of the responses did not mention either workmanship or human relations and organizational ties, but spoke of personal rewards of income, prospects, security, and of working conditions – suggesting that work was regarded more as a means than as an end in itself.

Of course, the particular type of work done will determine the possible sources of satisfaction, so that managers find the human relations part of their job more salient than do other engineers in industry, and teachers more frequently talk of their student contacts than of their subject. Similarly, in large firms, where a smaller proportion of the engineers tend to be in managerial functions, the theme of workmanship is mentioned more frequently. But for all categories of respondents in industry, whatever their background, attainment, or type of work, the vast majority find the job of engineering itself to be their major reward.

Sources of dissatisfaction

The high value placed on workmanship in the ideology of the engineer is shown even more clearly in that not only do engineering tasks predominate among work satisfactions, but it is the organization that emerges as chief villain when dissatisfactions are discussed. Indeed, lack of engineering know-how among superiors and colleagues is a major complaint. And when the work itself is cited as unsatisfactory this tends to be because workmanship is frustrated.

The majority of work frustrations and dissatisfactions were attributed to the organizational systems within which engineering is done, and especially to the calibre of the men employed by these organizations. The most frequent criticism, as might be expected, is of superiors, who are described as less than satisfactory in general terms or – more severely – as incompetent or lacking in technical knowledge and qualifications. Colleagues and subordinates are also frequently felt to be a problem because of their inadequacies and lack of skill and technical knowledge, as are clients and students. A related issue is the feeling of a shortage of skilled personnel, which is a more frequent complaint in smaller organizations. It would almost seem that, as far as the engineer is concerned, 'he who is not a technocrat is against me'. Other organizational deficiencies cited include the perennial bureaucratic bogy of 'red tape', the stifling of initiative, insufficient personal authority in decision-making, being responsible to too many superiors, and being subject to poor systems of communication.

Frustrations stemming from the work itself also suggest that craftsmanship is the decisive criterion. They include not having enough working time and not getting on with the job fast enough, as well as not having opportunity to exercise skill in the work being done. But under-utilization of professional skills and abilities is apparently felt less keenly among the engineers than other studies report (Kornhauser, 1962, p. 140), even though, when specifically asked, over half the sample agree that aspects of their work should be handled by someone with less training (see Chapter 5). It may be noted that when economic factors are referred to as frustrations, they are as likely to concern the limited capital for pursuing special projects as to be personal income dissatisfactions. Career frustrations – such as vague or limited promotion prospects – are among the most frequently mentioned problems, partly because, as we have seen in the analysis of mobility patterns, if organizational difficulties become too severe or if chances for advancement are poor, the engineer, being in a seller's market, does not suffer quietly where he is, but rather moves to a different career ladder or to a different firm.

One-sixth of the respondents claimed to have no major frustrations or dissatisfactions at work. The absence of complaints is spread fairly evenly over the career types. Those who did complain tended to be in the oldest age group (55+), were almost as likely to be graduates as non-graduates, and were as likely as not to be successful – indeed, there were more frustrations above the £3,000 income level than below it. Money does not invariably bring happiness.

Administrative versus technical orientation
The two themes of workmanship and human relations are part of a more fundamental dichotomy of career orientations, which has been distinguished in studies ranging from civil service bureaucracies (for example, Reissman, 1949) and labour unions (Wilensky, 1956) to research units (Pelz, 1956) and university faculties (Caplow & McGee, 1958). The contrast is between the professional or cosmopolitan and the organizational or local orientation. The two are differentiated in the extent to which there is loyalty to the employing organization, commitment to specialized role skills, and use of professional as opposed to organizational reference groups (Gouldner, 1957–58; Kornhauser, 1962, Chapter V; cf. Glaser, 1964). Most studies have emphasized the conflict between the orientations, but Kornhauser has argued that the division of labour in an organization not only is compatible with, but requires, a diversity of work orientations:

'There are at least three major functions to be performed if a professional speciality is to make a satisfactory contribution to the large enterprise of which it is a part: (1) *production* of technical results (e.g. scientific research); (2) *administration* of the conditions under which technical results are produced; (3) *application and communication* of technical results. Correlatively, it may be hypothesized that those who have a predominantly professional orientation tend to be strong producers of technical results; those who have a predominantly organizational orientation tend to assume administrative responsibilities; and those who seek to combine orientations to both organization and profession are especially capable of facilitating the utilization of technical results' (pp. 121–2).

The accordance between basic organizational needs and types of orientation would appear to be quite rational. But the empirical question remains of the distribution of types of orientation within an occupation and the availability of channels congruent with orientations.

To ascertain the direction of their aspirations and work orientation, the engineers were asked: 'Assuming the pay would be the same, would you prefer an administrative position or a primarily technical advisory position?' Two-fifths of the graduates and half the non-graduates expressed a preference for a technical post (42 per cent and 52 per cent respectively), the remainder being evenly divided between having a preference for the administrative side and desiring a combination of both. Among the graduates, those with first-class degrees have the strongest preference for the technical side.

Consistent with patterns found in other studies, the strength of administrative orientations among engineers increases with length of service and status in the organization:

'Scientists fresh from the academic world are more likely than those with considerable experience and high status to stress research as their personal goal. Once having seen that the larger rewards go to the managers, and having themselves experienced some upward mobility on the basis of assuming administrative responsibilities, they are more likely to make administration their personal goal' (Kornhauser, 1962, p. 138; cf. Marcson, 1960).

Thus, in the youngest group of engineers, three-fifths express a technical preference, the proportion dropping to just over a third in the oldest age group. Similar differences are associated with status and job function. Only a third of those with a high-status title state a technical preference, as compared with over half of those of lower status. As we have seen in Chapter 6 (*Table 21*), career type is also a major determinant of orientation, although it produces some striking anomalies between the type of work done and the desired ideal. Over a third of the managers express a technical preference, yet many of them are engaged in essentially non-technical work. And, although half of those in operations and almost two-thirds of those in RD and D would, if the pay were the same, prefer a technical advisory post, we have seen that there is a sizable income difference making the administrative post more attractive. Furthermore, most promotions reduce the technical work content. The evidence suggests, then, that the demands of organizations do not appear to be in harmony with the orientations of their professional employees, and that there is a need to create possible lines of promotion along professional rather than managerial hierarchies (see Kornhauser, 1962, pp. 143 ff.). Personal preferences for technical or administrative work, although related to which side is more highly esteemed, are not identical with such evaluations. In response to the question, 'Can you say whether you personally respect more an engineering colleague who rises to the ranks of top management or one who makes a major contribution to engineering technology?', almost half of the respondents are most impressed by the technological contribution, and only a fifth by the managerial rise; the remainder are unable to choose between the two. Again, such views are basic to the ideology of engineering, and are less influenced by factors of age, graduate status, and attainment than was the item on career orientation. Curiously, of those expressing an administrative career preference – towards which, in spite of the hypothetical pay equality, they are likely to have been biased by the occupational facts of life – as many reserve their respect for the technological contribution as for the managerial climb. Those whose orientation is technical are more consistent, with less than a fifth thinking much of the managerial attainment and more than three times that proportion evaluating the technological contribution more highly.

Those who feel that the attainment of a post in management warrants greater respect explain their sentiment by affirming that management is the more difficult job or, more specifically, that it requires qualities additional to technical ones. The implication of the latter remark would seem to be that management requires skills beyond the *mere* talents required for a technological contribution.

Management, it is felt, demands personality as well as knowledge, and requires a wider outlook. Only a tenth of management's admirers admitted their personal ambitions or the higher status or income of managerial posts to be the basis of their preference. Of those who admire the technological contribution more, half gave as their reason the greater difficulty of this accomplishment, the fact that it was a greater *personal* achievement – perhaps suggesting the notion of the rugged individualist as opposed to the organization man who admires other organization men. It is felt that few make a major technical contribution, whereas many whose achievements are unremarkable can get to the top of management – by pulling strings, with the aid of contacts or father's position, or simply by moving up rungs of the promotion ladder. Those who admire the managerial side claim that it takes special qualities, whereas the technologically oriented feel that anyone can administrate. Other reasons for the view that greater respect is due to the technological contribution underline the professional element. They include the feeling that such a contribution constitutes a service to the community, to engineering science, or even to mankind; that it involves the advancement of knowledge and placing the profession before personal career factors or obsessional status-seeking. The juxtaposition could almost be said to amount to truth and humanity on the side of technology as opposed to managerial greed.

The links between engineering and management in terms of both career patterns and managerial orientations have been frequently considered. Curiously, the engineer's commitment to professional and technical criteria, which we have seen to be much more pervasive, has received much less attention. Perhaps the observation that engineers are oriented to engineering does not appear particularly enlightening. Yet it has practical implications. Certainly there is need for more attention to questions concerning the sequence of commitments. It seems likely, for example, that many engineers climb the managerial ladder not necessarily because they are more interested in people than in things, but because their creative energies are not fully utilized in engineering work. They become managers not because they *have* an administrative orientation; rather, the orientation may develop in the face of limitations imposed upon the use of their engineering skills. It may well be that those pushed out of engineering work in this way become equally good managers as those drawn by the appeal of administrative responsibilities. But there can be little question that, as a result of this process, engineering research and development, if not operations, suffer from the outflow of capable men, many of whose technical abilities may not be appropriately employed in their managerial work. The serious implications of the situation are indicated in the conclusion of the 1963 report of the Committee on Scientific Manpower that there will be a fair balance between supply and demand in respect of scientists and technologists only if they do not take on management jobs where their qualifications are not of direct relevance. Yet rising productivity and a higher rate of industrial growth are resulting in an increasing proportion of scientists and technologists being employed in management (Advisory Council on Scientific Policy, 1963). Clearly the managerial-organizational and technical-professional orientations are both needed, but the way in which men and positions are matched at present puts the former at a premium and underestimates the potentials of the latter.

INTENSITY AND EXTENT OF COMMITMENT

Our questions about work satisfactions and dissatisfactions were intended to ascertain occupational themes rather than to estimate what proportions of the sample were or were not satisfied. That only a sixth volunteered that they had no major frustrations does not necessarily indicate that the remainder were generally dissatisfied with their work.

Comparison with other professions

Evidence from other studies concerning the extent of contentment on the part of technical professionals is somewhat contradictory. In the context of industry, it has been suggested that, owing to the conflict between orientations and organizational exigencies, the situation is less than happy:

'Normally the highest rewards go to those who assume administrative responsibility. In consequence, because of the increasingly large numbers of technical professionals in industry, many are doomed to disappointment even when they lean toward an organizational orientation, given the limited number of managerial positions Those who have a strong professional orientation are subject to a different kind of frustration, for their opportunities to gain high rewards *without* undertaking administrative tasks are even more limited. Here lies a clue to the relatively high level of job dissatisfaction expressed by industrial scientists and engineers' (Kornhauser, 1962, p. 128).

But an inquiry in the United States reports that 91 per cent of mathematicians, 89 per cent of physicists and biologists, and 86 per cent of chemists would choose the same kind of work if they were beginning their careers again. All these figures relating to scientists, the majority of whom work in industry, are higher than a comparable one for a free profession, law, where 83 per cent would repeat their choice (cited in Blauner, 1960). Another American report, however, finds that only 76 per cent of scientists and 63 per cent of engineers would, in retrospect, make the same career decision (Opinion Research Corporation, 1959). And Wilensky (1964*b*) records that 70 per cent of his engineers feel this way.

Responses to a similar question in our study showed the degree of commitment expressed by mechanical engineers to be considerably greater than that found in other studies of engineers and only slightly lower than that reported for scientists and lawyers: 78 per cent of the sample would, if they were faced with the choice a second time, choose engineering again rather than an alternative career. Whatever the career may connote for a particular individual, almost four-fifths of the respondents are glad that they entered this profession – an impressive degree of satisfaction. All but a sixth of those expressing a favourable commitment were firm about it – they would *definitely* stay in engineering if they were faced again with the option. Of those who were less committed, equal proportions thought that they would probably choose a different career or that an alternative career would definitely be preferable. The least committed are, of course, those who have actually left the profession. Their views might provide a useful supplement to our findings but the individuals concerned unfortunately fall outside the scope of the present sample.

Factors influencing commitment
The proportions of graduates and non-graduates who express a positive commitment are almost the same, with first-class graduates expressing least regrets about choice of career. Commitment increases with age, from 75 per cent of the youngest group to 83 per cent of the oldest. As one spends more time in a career the possibility of an alternative way of life becomes more remote. Commitment is not related to success, and differences between career types are

minimal: 82 per cent of those in operations, 80 per cent in non-industrial work, 78 per cent in management, and only 74 per cent in RD and D would repeat their career choice. That RD and D has the lowest proportion of committed individuals is a finding contrary to expectation. It appears to be contradicted by the fact that those who have a technical orientation are more committed than those who have an administrative preference (81 and 73 per cent respectively, compared with 78 per cent of those who have a mixed orientation). It may be that those in RD and D are less happy on account of the low rewards in this area and the under-utilization of skill in some RD and D positions. The technical orientation, it would appear, can frequently be better satisfied in work in areas other than RD and D, where prospects are better, and the type of work done is more challenging. Further evidence for this view is suggested by the relation between commitment and references to workmanship as the major source of job satisfaction. The most highly committed find engineering tasks their major source of satisfaction. But *routine* work is most likely to alienate the engineer, making him wish he had followed a different career.

The most highly committed think more highly of their profession than do other respondents. They accord engineering higher status *vis-à-vis* other occupations (see Chapter 7) than do their less optimistic colleagues. In contrast, the less committed, especially those who would definitely prefer a different occupation, reveal their estrangement by having little to do with professional associations and they even disdain to number engineering colleagues among their friends.

Of those who *would* stay in engineering if they had their time over again, a quarter would choose a different branch (cf. Havemann & West, 1952). Equal proportions of graduates and non-graduates think that they might be happier in a different branch; pass graduates are most keen on alternative possibilities.

Alternative career choices
The careers considered more desirable than engineering do not suggest any predominant type of preference. Only a small proportion of those who would reject engineering opt for a related type of work, such as one of the pure sciences, industrial management, or architecture. Most of the seemingly more attractive alternatives are entirely different occupations, mainly the established professions, such as law

and medicine. Accordingly, there is no indication that those with a low level of commitment to engineering are frustrated scientists or master-builders. Rather, they would appear to be contemplating pastures new, which they do not know but which, in comparison with the present field that they do know, might well be greener.

Evidence for high overall level of commitment
Retrospective considerations were applied not only to the initial making of a career choice, but also to the way in which the career path was followed. Most respondents (70 per cent) feel that their occupational career has ideally fitted them for their present job. Those who think that their past has been a less than ideal preparation do not focus their criticisms on any one issue. They mention short-comings in their educational background as well as in their industrial training period – deficiencies in practical experience, drawing-office work, etc. (see Chapter 4). There are also expressions of the wish for wider, more general experience and for training in management, and some regret that they have not pursued different specializations. The paucity and diffuseness of the expressed regrets are consistent with the high overall level of occupational commitment.

Perhaps the strongest indicator of commitment is thinking well enough of one's occupation to wish it upon one's children. As we have seen, almost a quarter of those with sons expect them to become engineers. Even without comparable figures from other professions, this proportion would appear to be of an impressive magnitude, indicative of a marked degree of satisfaction with engineering as an occupation.

On the basis of several criteria we have seen that career commit-ment, or satisfaction with engineering work, is generally positive. The extent to which this is oriented towards the work itself rather than to the engineering profession requires further study of the range of involvement in professional activities.

PROFESSIONAL ASSOCIATIONS

While the professional association does not serve the same function for the salaried professions as it does for the older self-employed ones, it is obvious that it has a key role as a qualifying association – the basis of admission to a professional body (Millerson, 1964). Although one need not be a member of the professional institution in order to be a mechanical engineer, the lack of such affiliation will severely hinder job possibilities. Engineering institutions, in common with other types of professional and scientific association, have a dual function: as learned societies they are committed to the advancement of knowledge; they are also concerned with a wide range of professional problems, such as the recruitment, utilization, and status of their members. This second function has been limited by their charters:

'Concentrating, as they have done, on "learned society" activities and the hall-marking of their members for competence in the subdivisions concerned, protection of status and interests were neglected and unity and monopoly have not been achieved' (*The Chartered Mechanical Engineer*, June 1963, p. 307).

Attitudes to professional engineering institutions

The proliferation of its professional societies is a particular problem of the engineering profession, manifesting a lack of unity. Nevertheless, two-thirds of the mechanical engineers were opposed to the idea of the various professional bodies getting together to see whether they could agree to amalgamate; that is, they objected to a mere getting together of the different branches for initial discussions. The main reason for their negative attitude was the feeling that many distinct interests and problems were involved, for which specialization was necessary; and that a large amalgamated association would necessarily be inefficient and unwieldy. Those in favour of exploring the possibility of amalgamation – older graduates, who themselves belonged to more than one institution – keenly felt that such a professional union would be a source of strength, aiding the status of engineers, avoiding considerable duplication of effort, eliminating waste due to professional jealousy, and raising professional standards of qualification.

Extent and degree of participation

Owing to the method of sample selection, all respondents are members of the Institution of Mechanical Engineers – 70 per cent corporate members and 30 per cent graduate members. Whether an individual is a corporate member of his professional institution is more than anything else a function of his age – all over 45 are corporate members. For the younger men, corporate membership is related to graduate status, class of degree, attainment of success, and working in a managerial position or in a non-industrial setting. The same factors identify the individual who is a corporate member of more than one institution, which is true of half the respondents over the age of 45. No other single engineering institution included more than 8 per cent of the mechanicals: only three, in fact – the Electrical and Production Engineers' Institutions and the Royal Aeronautical Society – could claim as many as 5 per cent of the sample. Even the Engineers' Guild, the one organization that cuts across the structure of specializations and is specifically concerned with problems of status and income – its object being 'to promote and maintain the unity, public usefulness, honour, and interests of the engineering profession' – involves but 3 per cent of our respondents.

When the number of institutions to which respondents belong is related to their degree of activity in each (holding office, attending meetings, etc.), the usual organizational phenomenon emerges of a small number of people doing most of the work: some two-thirds admit to being inactive members, a seventh claim to be moderately active, and only a fifth boast of being very active. A finding that accords with those of other studies (Kornhauser, 1962, Chapter 4), and with the learned-society function of a professional association, is that active participation is greatest on the part of graduates, especially those with the highest class of degree, and on the part of respondents in non-industrial settings. Among those in industry, in conformity with their broader professional interests, activity is greater on the part of the more successful from the ranks of management. Nevertheless, in comparison with their non-industrial counterparts, industrial managers tend to be somewhat more superficially involved, for though they have collected a larger number of institution memberships, they are not as frequently represented among the active participants.

Participation in the activities of engineering institutions may be regarded as an aspect of the engineer's professional orientation and interest, but it does not necessarily imply a high level of personal commitment nor is it the only way in which he can contribute to the profession. For example, frequent attendance at meetings or the acquisition of a large number of memberships may reflect no more than the policy of a firm that encourages these things. Moreover, since the engineer is a member of a profession with academic-scientific foundations, his productivity embraces not only his everyday work – which may very well reveal creativity as well as organizational attainment – but also publications, inventions, and lectures.

PROFESSIONAL PRODUCTIVITY

The total amount of activity in this sphere is greater than that in institution affairs, but it is found, nevertheless, that less than half of the individuals do all of the work, as shown in *Table 29*. Apart from

TABLE 29 Productivity (publications, papers or lectures, and patented inventions) by graduate status

	Graduates	Non-graduates
	%	%
Publications, lectures & inventions	6	4
Publications & lectures	9	3
Publications & inventions	5	2
Lectures & inventions	6	3
Publications only	10	4
Lectures only	11	10
Inventions only	8	12
None	45	62
	100	100

the category of no productivity, in which non-graduates are heavily over-represented, the differences between graduates and non-graduates are smaller than might be anticipated.

Inventions, publications, lectures
Patented inventions, in many ways the product *par excellence* of the engineer, stand out from the other items in that it is only here that the non-graduate outdoes the graduate, and that the younger man working in operations or RD and D does more than the older man in a managerial or non-industral post. It should be noted, however, that this finding is limited to those who have inventions only to their credit. When all those who have patented inventions are considered (whether or not they have also published or given papers), the proportion of graduates is somewhat greater than that of non-graduates (25 per cent vs. 21 per cent). Other correlates for the production of inventions are on the whole similar to those for the other types of professional productivity – publications and papers or lectures. All these professional activities are more frequent on the part of men

who are older, who hold a higher-class degree, who are highly paid or at least successful, who are active in their professional institutions, and who read more technical journals than do their non-productive colleagues.

By contrast, among Purdue engineering graduates younger men – those within fifteen years of graduation – were found to be most creative in terms of patent applications. Scholarship was a key determinant: 40 per cent of those in the top fifth of their class reported one or more patents as compared with 27 per cent of those in the remaining four-fifths. The authors' observations that a patent is not the only criterion of creativeness, since numerous designs and discoveries are not patentable, and that many engineers display equal ingenuity in the performance of their jobs are well taken and would no doubt be found to be applicable to many in our sample who have been classed as unproductive (Hawkins *et al.*, 1959).

Of the graduates, 30 per cent have publications to their credit, and an equal proportion have presented papers or lectures, the comparable proportions for non-graduates being only 13 per cent and 20 per cent. That more engineers have not produced patented inventions, given the proportion who have published and presented papers, runs counter to the generally held unacademic image of the engineering profession. For the second type of productivity is clearly more scientific and academic than it is industrial. The Institution of Mechanical Engineers in fact found its 'publish or penalty' policy ineffectual only eight years after it was written into the founding rules (Millerson, 1964, p. 68). Few academic societies would find such a rule workable.

Productivity in relation to career types and orientation
There is some correspondence between the three types of productivity (publications, papers or lectures, inventions) and the major work functions and types of orientation in engineering. A record of publications is most frequent on the part of those who are in non-industrial positions or management, and it is associated with having a mixed technical-administrative orientation. The presentation of papers and lectures is more often the prerogative of managers than it is of those in non-industrial posts – the former being more likely to give public lectures and the latter, mostly academics, bearing the brunt of publications. Largely because of the role of managers, this type of productivity tends to be associated with either an administra-

tive or a mixed orientation. Inventions being almost as frequently produced by those in RD and D as by present holders of managerial posts, the orientation of inventors tends to be technical.

Work-connected reading

Whether the engineer contributes to his science or not, it is an ongoing one and keeping up with it requires some degree of effort. Although 8 per cent of the sample claim to read more than ten professional journals regularly, 20 per cent admit to reading none at all. The remainder are almost equally divided into those who read one or two, those who read three or four, and those who read between five and nine journals. There is, strangely, very little difference according to class of degree or, for that matter, between graduates and nongraduates: even one-fifth of the first-class graduates read no technical journals regularly. Similarly, equal proportions of the successful and the unsuccessful admit that they read no journals, but more of the unsuccessful read one or two, while the successful tend to claim that they read three or more. Those working in RD and D are the most likely to read at least some professional journals and older men most readily admit that they are regular readers of none. Perhaps, however, 'regular' reading is not the type of reading that the engineer must do in attempting to obtain solutions to problems he is working with. The range of journals read is extensive, representing the publications of a host of specialities. Only *The Chartered Mechanical Engineer*, *The Engineer*, and *Engineering* are read by at least a quarter of the respondents. Foreign language journals (not including American) are read by only three individuals out of 977, suggesting that even those people of foreign origin in the sample have taken up the characteristically British attitude of insularity.

FRIENDSHIP PATTERNS

The inclusion of professional colleagues among one's intimate friends is both an additional indicator of commitment and a mechanism that reinforces other types of commitment (Gerstl, 1961a). Respondents were asked for the occupations of their three closest friends and they were grouped according to whether none was an engineer, two or all three were engineers, or only one was an engineer. One-third of responses fall into each of these categories; there are virtually no differences between graduates and non-graduates, although honours graduates are more likely to have at least some engineers among their friends. The likelihood of a high colleague ambience is much greater for the younger man, being most frequent among those working in operations and thus related to a technical orientation. It is to a considerable extent determined by having a large number of colleagues at one's place of work. The absence of a professional ambience is strongly associated with a low commitment: half of those with no colleagues among their friends express regrets or doubts about their career choice as compared with less than three-tenths of those who have engineering friends. The reinforcement effect of having colleagues among one's friends does not, contrary to expectations, influence professional productivity or the amount of status accorded to engineering in comparison with other occupations. The limited intrusion of the work of the engineer upon his personal relations and social life will be considered in more detail in the next chapter.

CHAPTER 9

The engineer off duty

The account up to this point of the engineer's origins, education, and world of work does not complete the description implied in the phrase 'the anatomy of a profession'. The influence of one's occupation is not limited to behaviour at the place of work nor is it restricted to the hours between nine and five. The area that remains to be considered is the way in which work affects private life and the extent to which membership in a particular occupational milieu permeates other aspects of daily activity.

An analysis of leisure and related activities serves other purposes in addition to indicating the links between work and non-work roles. An occupation affords its incumbents a social status which allows, and to a certain extent dictates, a particular style of life. For the engineer, this pattern is clearly a middle-class one. Accordingly, the account of the engineer's leisure is not pertinent only to his particular occupation. Rather, the engineer is representative of the species of salaried professionals. Just as his work life is in many respects similar to that of non-engineers in comparable organizational contexts, so is his leisure.

At the same time, there are divergent trends between occupations and even within the ranks of one occupation. For lack of comparative evidence, the amount of variation between engineering and other occupational groups must remain largely speculative, but among engineers many of the factors that have served to explain contrasting patterns at work also apply to the realm of leisure. Thus it is necessary to consider such questions as to what extent does the attainment of a university degree or the pursuit of a particular career line influence one's style of life and one's attitudes as well as one's career?

Although our concern with leisure is mainly in terms of the influence of occupational role, non-occupational factors are involved at the same time. Leisure patterns, as will be indicated, vary strongly by age. Family status is probably even more important. In this respect, the engineers are a relatively homogeneous group. All but

8 per cent are married. Of those over the age of 35, all but 4 per cent are married, as are all but 17 per cent of those under 35. Thus, most typically, the engineer is a family man. Over four-fifths of those over 35 have children. The four age groups we have used correspond to the stages of the life cycle: the modal patterns are for the youngest age group to have pre-school-age children; for the second age group to have school-age children; and for the children of those in the two older age categories to be in secondary or higher education or to have left school. Although the educational background of the respondents themselves has an influence upon the life cycle in that graduates tend to marry later than non-graduates (Rapoport, 1964), this difference becomes negligible in subsequent stages of family life.

The portrayal of leisure activities that follows is undertaken essentially in terms of its range – from the narrow circle of family (the Englishman in his castle-home) outwards to informal and formal involvement with the larger community (Havighurst & Feigenbaum, 1959). The analysis of leisure patterns is followed by an examination of other non-work aspects of life, including consumption patterns and attitudes in the areas of politics, taste, and religion.

HOME LIFE AND TV VIEWING

Under the broad heading of leisure, probably no time is more difficult to account for than that spent 'at home' in activities which may be routine, and yet may not occupy set periods of time. In recognition of this, the question used in this area was a very general one: 'About how much time do you spend each week doing jobs around your home, on your car, or working in your garden?'

One-quarter of all respondents claim to spend under five hours a week in this type of activity, a third spend between five and ten hours, a quarter ten to fifteen hours, and the remaining fifth even longer. Younger men spend more time in home-centred activities, as might be expected at this stage of family life. But there is also a difference between graduates and non-graduates, suggesting divergent life styles between the two groups. The non-graduates, especially the less successful ones, tend to be more home centred than the graduates. There is, curiously, almost no relationship between the length of the working week and the number of hours estimated for tasks around the house.

Extensive TV viewing, in combination with spending a great deal of time in tasks around the house, would identify the home-centred individuals with the strongest segregation of work and leisure, possibly representing the less mobile sector of the profession. The amount of time attributed to TV viewing by the sample as a whole is, however, strangely low. Furthermore, although engineers are a relatively affluent portion of the population, only 82 per cent own TV sets, while the figure for the total British population is 86 per cent (*The Listener*, 19 April 1962, p. 710). Both the mean and the modal TV viewing patterns for the engineers are to have watched only between five and nine hours in the week preceding the interview, whereas the national average weekly viewing time over the winter and spring months (including, it should be noted, women and children viewers as well as men) is about fifteen hours (*The Listener*, 19 July 1962, p. 119). Only 6 per cent of the engineers say that they watched TV for fifteen or more hours in the previous week, some half watched between five and fourteen hours, almost a third less than five hours, and the rest (16 per cent) say that they did not watch at all.

As with tasks around the home, there is again a difference between graduates and non-graduates, although the two are equally represented among the very infrequent and the very frequent viewers. Non-graduates, however, tend to cluster in the middle (five to fourteen hours) viewing category, whereas graduates are twice as likely as non-graduates to be non-viewers.

Contrary to expectations, hours of TV viewing are not related to level of aspiration as defined by the highest position that an individual hopes to reach in his career. Those who hope to move furthest in their careers are not spending fewer hours in this way. Rather, viewing patterns are more directly a function of present position held and the corresponding life styles which such positions would appear to require. Thus the home-centred pattern, in terms of both tasks around the house and TV viewing, tends to be that of the less successful non-graduate working in operations or in RD and D. The frequent TV viewers, for example, are twice as likely to be earning under £1,800 as to be earning over this amount, while those in the top income group tend to have watched TV for fewer than four hours or not at all. Successful men, especially those in management and in non-industrial posts, pursue leisure patterns which take them more frequently outside the confines of family life (cf. Hodges, 1964).

HOBBIES

Although the term 'hobby' refers to an activity that is not one's main business, hobbies are frequently connected with work. Similarly, though the derivation from hobby-horse connotes frivolity, many hobbies today have become very serious matters (Larrabee, 1958). We used the term for the whole gamut of major leisure-time interests. As with other aspects of leisure, both the range of interests shown and the degree to which they converge with work activities are of primary concern.

The engineers are very highly represented in a wide range of hobby activities. Only 2 per cent profess to have no interest that might be considered a hobby. While pursuit of hobbies is characteristic of middle-class patterns of leisure (Cauter & Downham, 1954), the degree and range of the engineers' participation (as shown in *Table 30*, which includes numerous multiple responses) would appear to be above average.

TABLE 30   Major leisure-time interests

	%
Reading connected with work	73
Other reading	82
Music	44
Sport	55
Crafts (do-it-yourself, etc.)	27
Photography	32
Languages	11
Work-connected hobbies	23
Other hobbies	29
No hobby interests	2

It is most striking that almost three-quarters of the respondents claim work-connected reading to be one of their hobby interests. Equally notable is the fact that educational background is not associated with keeping up with one's field: non-graduates are as likely to do this as are graduates. For both groups, of those who do some work-connected reading, half devote ten hours or more a week to it and almost a third spend less than five hours in this way. Some of this reading may be done in company time, but the label 'leisure-time interest' indicates that most of it is done at home and suggests a convergence between work and leisure activities.

The likelihood of doing *some* work-connected reading decreases with advanced age (from 79 per cent of those under 35 to 66 per cent of those aged 55 and over). It is more common among the less successful, perhaps in an attempt to become more successful. It is most prevalent among those in RD and D and in non-industrial posts, who are in fact financially less successful, and whose type of work intrinsically requires keeping up with new developments. Those in non-industrial posts, mainly academics, are the most likely to do some work-connected reading, and also, since they have more 'company time' available, they devote longer hours to such reading.

Hobbies connected with the field of engineering or some aspect of work were mentioned by just under a quarter of the respondents. (The classifying of an activity as work-connected or otherwise was done by the respondent.) While comparative figures are lacking, it is unlikely that other professions afford equal opportunities for work-connected hobbies; for many hobbies followed by non-engineers have something to do with engineering in the loose sense of the term.

Pursuing a work-connected hobby is not influenced by age, but those over 45 tend to devote more time to their interest once they do get involved. Differences between graduates and non-graduates are slight, but non-graduates more frequently have a work-connected hobby. Contrary to expectation, this type of hobby is hardly more likely for the man in RD and D than it is for those in management, operations, or in non-industrial posts. This finding may well be a result of unequal opportunities for the expression of an interest in engineering 'workmanship' at work. For example, the manager who is divorced from engineering tasks in his job may find satisfaction from an engineering-type hobby. Conversely, the man in RD and D who in a sense practises his hobby through his work will be less motivated to continue it in his leisure.

The link between work and leisure is clearly very strong as shown in that three-quarters of the engineers include work-connected reading among their major leisure-time activities and a quarter carry over their engineering orientation (as either work supplements or work complements) into the realm of hobbies.

140 · *Engineers: the anatomy of a profession*

SOCIAL CIRCLES

Both frequency and range of social ties are indicative of the influence of work upon the realm of leisure and the relation between status at work and style of life. Social get-togethers with relatives not living in the household, although less common for older respondents, reveal a common pattern among all types of engineers: two-fifths of the sample had such contact in the month prior to interview. This figure is somewhat lower than that reported in a study of East London (Young & Willmott, 1957) where almost half the sample visited relatives weekly. Interestingly, American figures are quite similar to the East London ones (Axelrod, 1956). The lower rates of meeting with relatives on the part of engineers are likely to be a reflection both of the less family-centred middle-class style of life and of their geographical mobility and consequent separation from relatives.

While younger men spend more of their time with family obligations, older respondents maintain wider social networks with colleagues from work, other professional colleagues, neighbours, and other friends. For all respondents, the most common social ties are with 'other friends' (over two-thirds had such social contacts in the month prior to the interview), followed by colleagues from work (for three-fifths), neighbours (for over half), and other professional colleagues (for just under half). These figures indicate a generally active social life among engineers and show the convergence of work and leisure roles in the frequent social ties with colleagues.

Similar factors account for the higher rates of contact with colleagues, with neighbours, and with other friends. All types of social relations are more frequent for graduates than for non-graduates, especially for those of higher-status social origins. Indeed, differences by social origins are greater than are those of educational background. The differences would appear to correspond to upper-middle- as opposed to middle-class life styles, and are most marked with respect to the widest circle of social life, that of 'other friends'.

Career factors are as important as origins and education in explaining alternative patterns of social relations. The successful, in all cases, have had more social contacts than the unsuccessful. While occupational success is associated with more social life of all types, it is most pronounced for colleague contacts – for both colleagues worked with and other professional colleagues. The more successful thus tend more to fuse work and leisure relationships.

As might be expected both from the nature of their occupational role and from the nature of their background characteristics, it is the managerial personnel who have the widest and most active social life. They are not, however, much more likely than others in industry to associate with colleagues from work. Those not in industry, on the other hand, see least of their colleagues from work. A similar pattern is reported among American chemists: those in academic settings see least of fellow chemists, although they see more of their work fellows, i.e. non-chemist academics (Strauss & Rainwater, 1962).

VOLUNTARY ASSOCIATIONS: CLUBS AND ORGANIZATIONS

By the nature of his employment, the engineer is almost invariably an 'organization man', for he tends to be an employee of some large entity, whether an industrial firm, the civil service, or a university. In his social life, however, apart from his membership of the Institution of Mechanical Engineers (an activity related more to his work life than to his leisure), he is no more likely to be a member of a voluntary association than is the average middle-class London suburbanite (Willmott & Young, 1960).

Only half of the engineers belong to any club or organization other than their professional institution. Just as the British as a whole are less likely to be 'joiners' than are Americans, so the engineer in Britain is less likely to have formal community ties than is his counterpart in the United States: only 20 per cent of Purdue engineering graduates say that they do not participate in any type of community activity (Lebold *et al.*, 1960).

Thus the extent of involvement in community life is but moderate. However, those who do belong to some formal groups tend to belong to more than one, and are likely to be active in organizational affairs in holding office, attending meetings, etc. Graduates and nongraduates reveal different patterns of participation. Because of this disparity, the types of voluntary association membership are shown separately for the two groups (*Table 31*). It may be seen that graduates are more likely to belong to *some* voluntary association, and that they tend to choose different associations from those chosen by nongraduates. Cultural, church, and political groups all include a much larger proportion of graduates, indicating disparity of both taste and of style of life. Interest in cultural groups of various types would appear to be a by-product of a university experience (and is unrelated to class of degree). Career types do not have a marked

TABLE 31   Membership of non-professional clubs and organizations by graduate status

Organization	Graduates	Non-graduates
	%	%
Church groups	25	18
Lodges and social clubs	18	19
Cultural groups (art, theatre, etc.)	17	9
Political organizations	11	6
Trade unions	5	9
Charitable groups	5	5
Ex-servicemen's groups	6	5
Hobby clubs	4	5
Other groups	4	2
Total mentions	95	78
All mentioning one or more groups	55	45

influence upon type of organizational affiliation, except that lodges and social clubs are somewhat more common for successful managers·

Active participation in professional organizations is strongly associated with activity in non-professional organizations – the syndrome of 'joiner'. Of more striking significance is the fact that similar factors account for participation in both types of group. The exceptions to this are that holding a first-class degree and being successful are associated with active participation in professional societies, but not with other types of organizational affiliation. The likelihood of all types of organizational activity increases with age (only two-fifths of those under 35 belong to a voluntary group as compared with almost two-thirds of those aged 55 and over), with graduate status, with high-status social origins, and with working in managerial and non-industrial posts. Apart from the case of social clubs, organizational involvement is not a function of success, although those in the highest income groups are highly represented in charitable and political groups.

LEISURE VALUES

The foregoing account of the use of leisure time has shown some of the variations resulting from age, differences in background, and career factors. In light of the numbers pursuing work-connected hobbies, the extent of work-connected reading, and the frequency of inclusion of colleagues among social contacts, it has been suggested that engineers manifest a considerable convergence of their work and leisure roles. This conclusion is based upon actual uses of time and types of social tie maintained. A related issue concerns the relative *value* placed upon 'pure' leisure, as opposed to the use of spare time for work-connected activities or for work itself. The question used for this purpose was: 'If you had two more hours in the day, a 26-hour day, what would you most like to do with the extra time?' It cannot be assumed that an answer to this hypothetical question would correspond with what an individual actually would do if he had additional time. But, at their face value, responses indicate what the engineers think they would like to do, or what they feel they do not devote sufficient time to at present. Responses, which were, interestingly, similar for graduates and non-graduates, are shown in *Table 32.*

TABLE 32   Hypothetical use of two extra hours

	%
Relaxation, rest, sleep	19
Time with family, at home	18
Hobby or recreation, sport	24
Cultural activities	8
Recreational reading	15
Total 'pure' leisure	84
Work-connected reading, education	7
Work activities	5
Total work-connected leisure	12
Other responses, don't know	4
Total	100
No. of responses (multiple)	1,198

The high value placed upon 'pure' leisure activities is striking: only 12 per cent of the responses refer to work activities or to work-connected reading or further education. (The figure would be only slightly higher had work-connected hobbies been distinguished from other hobbies.) Thus, although three-quarters of the engineers actually do some work-connected reading, all but 7 per cent apparently feel that they do a sufficient amount. Even if they had more time available, they would not expect to do more.

On the basis of their responses to this item, and in spite of the convergence of work and leisure roles shown by the actual uses of leisure time, the engineers would not seem to place a high value upon work and work-connected activities. Their preference for pure leisure is considerably greater than that voiced by other occupational groups. For example, Clarke (1956), using a similar question, found that 20 per cent of higher prestige occupational groups chose work. Similarly, in another American study (Gerstl, 1961b), 50 per cent of academics and 18 per cent of organization men but only 9 per cent of dentists opted for work and work-connected reading. Much of the difference is due to the alternative meanings of work even among high-status occupations. But the discrepancy between British and American findings may also reflect different values placed upon leisure in Britain and the United States.

Of those who would devote their extra hours to work-connected reading or further education, equal proportions come from all age groups, levels of success, and types of career. But this expectation is slightly higher among the non-graduates (8 per cent) than it is among the graduates (5 per cent). While identical proportions of graduates and non-graduates wish to spend the extra time working, this tendency increases slightly with age, even more with income, and is most frequent for those in managerial posts.

Responses indicating a preference for pure leisure activities are similar in pattern to responses concerning actual uses of leisure time. Non-graduates are somewhat more home centred in wanting more time with their families, whereas graduates, especially successful managers, are more interested in additional time for cultural activities.

Only 5 per cent of the engineers state that they would, if given extra hours, devote them to work. This view is in conformity with an internalized level of motivation: it is highly related to levels of aspiration, in terms of both highest position expected and highest income expected. Although it is expressed by only a small part of the sample – and the small numbers with this degree of work commitment are themselves significant of the orientation of engineers – it suggests another type of work and leisure connexion, that between level of aspiration and use of leisure time for work.

POLITICAL ATTITUDES

In considering the engineer as a political man, American studies suggest that he *is* different from his status counterpart in other occupational roles (Lipset, 1960; Kornhauser, 1962). For example, in a comparison of scientists and engineers with similar social origins, religious affiliation, and parental political preference, 60 per cent of the scientists were found to have voted Democratic, while 80 per cent of the engineers had voted Republican. That the political values of engineers are closer to those of management than are the values of scientists is shown not only by party preference but by other indicators of liberalism as well.

Social-class position is a key factor in explaining political orientation. In terms of his occupational role, as has been indicated, the engineer is clearly middle class. More specifically, he represents a highly mobile segment of his class, almost half of the non-graduates and over a fifth of the graduates coming from working-class backgrounds. Thus there are two major, yet opposite, forces shaping the engineer's predispositions: his present status and his social origins. Present status position is especially significant in the middle class which, in Britain, shows more class solidarity in political orientation than does the working class, 85 per cent of the middle class favouring the Conservatives (Abrams & Rose, 1960; Blondel, 1963). Obviously all members of the middle class have social origins, but a smaller proportion have working-class origins compared with the engineers as a whole.

Our analysis involves not actual voting behaviour, but political preference, in response to the question: 'Which political party do you think is best for people like yourself?' In June 1962 the national Gallup Poll figures in response to this question resulted in: Conservatives, 28 per cent; Labour, 34 per cent; Liberal, 18 per cent; and 'Don't know', 19 per cent. A similar proportion of engineers chose not to express a preference. Of those that did, over three-fifths (62 per cent) chose the Conservative party, only 11 per cent Labour, and over a quarter (27 per cent) chose the Liberal party. The high proportion in favour of the Liberals is most striking, even given that the survey took place when Liberal support was at its height, for under a fifth of the general public at that time gave allegiance to the Liberals. Accordingly, the type of person represented by the engineer would appear the cornerstone of Liberal support.

In terms of overall preference, the small amount of support given to Labour by engineers is a typical middle-class pattern. The Liberal support would thus appear to be at the expense of the Tories. Although the engineers' social origins account in a large measure for both Labour and Tory preferences, it is interesting to note that they have very little connexion with Liberal preferences.

Age has a very strong influence upon political orientation for at least two reasons. Older respondents tend to come from higher status origins, and, with increasing age, origins matter less and the individual's own social position matters more. While support for both the Labour party and the Liberals declines with age, the decline is much more dramatic for Labour, dwindling almost to the point of disappearance for the oldest age group.

Differences between graduates and non-graduates are not strong. There is somewhat more of a Tory preference among the graduates, but it is mainly a function of their social origins. Liberal support, although unconnected with origins, is, interestingly, greater among the non-graduates (29 per cent vs. 20 per cent among graduates). Success should be less important than social origins in explaining preference, since even the less successful man has the social status of a professional. Nevertheless, there is a strong association between success and a Tory preference. More interestingly, low success is more likely to be reflected in a Liberal preference than it is in one for Labour. The Liberals would seem to represent the social protest of the less successful professional.

Career types, which correspond somewhat to differential origins and more directly to differential rewards, are reflected in political attitudes in the high association between managerial posts and Tory support. Labour is favoured equally by those in the three types of career, while those in RD and D stand out as the keenest Liberal supporters – a preference expressed by almost two-fifths of their number.

NEWSPAPERS AND WEEKLIES READ

The type of newspaper that an individual reads reveals, apart from political preference, the general level of his intellectual taste, or what has been called 'brow level' (Lynes, 1955; Gerstl, 1961*b*). In Britain, as in many other countries, there is a distinction, both in content and in size of circulation, between the quality papers and those of mass circulation. On the one hand, there are the newspapers of 'top people': *The Times*, as well as *The Guardian* and *The Financial Times*. On the other hand, there are the mass circulation papers with the 'daily' prefix: *Daily Express, Daily Mail, Daily Mirror*, and *Daily Sketch*. *The Daily Telegraph* is outside this classification, in respect of both content and circulation, as also was the *Daily Herald*.

As shown by his newspaper reading habits, the engineer is by no means a top person or a highbrow; he is much less so, in fact, than is the architect, for whom comparable figures are available (Abrams, 1964). Neither, however, does the engineer's taste correspond with that of the general public. The differences between national newspaper preferences and those of the engineer are shown in *Table 33*. The

TABLE 33   Daily newspaper readership: the engineers and the public

	Engineers	National readership[a]
	%	%
Daily Herald	1	13
Daily Express	24	33
Daily Mail	16	19
Daily Mirror	6	37
The Daily Telegraph	39	9
Daily Sketch	4	10
The Times	5	3
The Guardian	13	3
The Financial Times	6	6
Total mentions	114	128

[a] Indep. Practitioners in Advertising Readership Survey, July 1961–June 1962.

typical engineer is a middlebrow in that he is more likely to read *The Daily Telegraph* than any other paper. An equally large proportion are readers of either the *Daily Mail* or the *Daily Express*, and only a quarter of all engineers read one of the quality papers. The low readership of the *Daily Herald* and the *Daily Mirror* is explained by the small amount of Labour political preference on the part of engineers. (The *Daily Herald* ceased publication in 1964.)

Differences among engineers themselves are almost as great as those between the 'typical' engineer and the public. The greatest contrast is once again between graduates and non-graduates: one-fifth of the latter read one of the quality papers, this proportion doubling for the graduates. Graduates are also more likely to read *The Daily Telegraph* than all the other mass dailies combined, whereas the reverse is true for non-graduates.

Among engineers, top people, in terms of income, do tend to read *The Times*, but *The Financial Times* even more, and they also read *The Daily Telegraph*. Reading *The Times* is more common in the context of non-industrial employment, while working in industrial management and reading *The Financial Times* are highly associated. Those in RD and D have singular tastes in newspapers as well as (and corresponding to their) politics. They are much less likely than anyone else to read the *Telegraph* and are most highly disposed towards *The Guardian*.

On Sundays there is a similar pattern of readership of quality papers and others. Indeed, on the basis of Sunday papers, the contrast between the engineer and the public is greater than that indicated by the daily papers, just as the taste levels on Sundays are more obvious. Again, the engineer emerges as at least a middlebrow: the most common Sunday paper read, by over two-fifths, is the *Sunday Express*. But reading *The Sunday Times* and/or *The Observer* is mentioned by over half the sample (no doubt partly on account of the amount of space these papers devote to job advertisements in technical fields), whereas less than a quarter admit to 'reading' any of the mass pictorial sensationals and even fewer mention *The Sunday Telegraph*.

Readership of quality papers tends to be the pattern for the graduates, the successful, and the highly paid. *The Sunday Telegraph* occupies a middle position, read equally by graduates and non-graduates, by the successful and the unsuccessful; the non-graduates and the less successful read the *Sunday Express* most frequently as well as the sensational pictorials. The RD and D men, consistent with their previously mentioned singularity, are more inclined to *The Observer* than to *The Sunday Times*.

Weeklies in Britain do not have mass circulations, and are not read by a large number of the engineers. The two that have the highest readership are, however, of special interest because they are work-connected. The two, *The Economist* and *The New Scientist*, correspond to different types of work function and orientation. Both are read more by graduates than by non-graduates, and more by graduates with better degrees. Both are associated with success, but much more so in the case of *The Economist*. Similarly, *The Economist* is read most by those in managerial posts, and *The New Scientist* by those in RD and D and in non-industrial positions. *The New Scientist* is read by a quarter of the first-class graduates (18 per cent of all graduates, 12 per cent of non-graduates), and *The Economist* by 12 per cent of those in management (10 per cent of all graduates, 14 per cent of first-class graduates, 5 per cent of non-graduates).

RELIGION

The nature of religious affiliation and involvement reveals another dimension of life style. In terms of nominal affiliation, church attendance, and intensity of belief, the trends for engineers are remarkably similar to those reported in national studies (Social Survey, Gallup Poll, 1963; Carr-Saunders, 1958; Pierce, 1964). Indeed, in the area of religious life, the engineer represents less the specifically middle-class pattern than the composite Briton.

Just like the general public, some three-fifths of the engineers claim affiliation with the Church of England, 7 per cent with the Scottish Church, and 7 per cent deny any religious affiliation. However, the engineers differ in being under-represented among Roman Catholics and over-represented among non-conformists (16 per cent of the engineers are non-conformists and 5 per cent are Roman Catholics, the difference in each case from the corresponding figure for the general public being 6 per cent).

Although national figures for church attendance are not entirely satisfactory, various surveys do reflect generally similar tendencies. As is the case in the national pattern, a quarter of the engineers claim to attend church fortnightly or weekly (the engineers being more prone than others to attend weekly) and over a tenth claim monthly attendance. Like the typical Briton, over three-fifths of the engineers do not attend church with any regularity. But the modal trend, for two-fifths of the engineers, is to attend church several times a year, a pattern pursued by only a quarter of the general public. Whereas only a fifth of the engineers profess not to attend church at all, the national proportion is twice as large. The differences between the engineer and the public are explained by the engineer's class in society. But the high degree of similarity between the engineers and the public suggests that class influences are not very important in this context.

Among the engineers themselves, frequency of church attendance is associated with social origins, and it is also affected slightly by age, the older generation, especially when of higher social origins, being somewhat more likely to attend weekly. But a greater difference is found between graduates and non-graduates, again indicating the different life styles of the two groups. Almost a quarter of the non-graduates do not attend church, compared with only 16 per cent of the graduates; a third of the graduates profess at least fortnightly attendance, compared with less than a quarter of the non-graduates.

Differential patterns of church attendance are not influenced by career type or by success (nor does increased church attendance result in more success).

Type of religious affiliation is, of course, very highly related to church attendance. The Roman Catholics attend most regularly, followed by the non-conformists, and the members of the Church of Scotland; the lowest attendance rate is for the Church of England.

Intensity of religious belief was ascertained by asking the respondent for a rating of the importance or unimportance of religion in his life on a twelve-point scale (the Staple scale). The two highest ratings have been labelled 'devout', the remaining positive ones 'moderate', and all the rest 'indifferent'. One-quarter of the engineers are devout, two-fifths are moderate, and one-third are indifferent regarding the importance of religion in their lives. The engineer in his religious belief is again very like the typical British male; he resembles him more closely in fact, than he does the typical incumbent of the professional-managerial class.

While intensity of belief, as shown by responses to this item, and religious behaviour, as indicated by church attendance, are closely related, the two dimensions show some interesting discrepancies. The proportions of the devout among graduates and non-graduates are similar, but the graduates are more likely to be indifferent while the non-graduates tend more to be moderate. Yet the graduates attend church more frequently than the non-graduates. This would seem to indicate that their church attendance is less a matter of greater piety

than a pattern of conformity or an outward display of middle-class
life style.

CONSUMPTION PATTERNS

The analysis of consumer patterns of engineers is concerned with
type of dwelling occupied and ownership of particular durable goods
as further indicators of life style in the middle-class 'standard package' (Riesman & Rosenborough, 1955). Whatever the content of the
standard consumption package, living accommodation constitutes a
major share, with age and income the most important determining
factors.

A majority of the engineers (55 per cent) are in the process of
buying their present accommodation and over a quarter (27 per cent)
have already done so. Whereas 18 per cent of those in the lowest
income category are in fully-owned homes, the figure rises to 53 per
cent of those in the highest income group. But even in the lowest
income category, 71 per cent either are buying or have bought their
home; 87 per cent of those in the top income group are in a similar
situation. These high figures explain the high degree of home orientation that has been previously noted.

Ownership of durable goods among the engineers is well above
national averages. For most items, with TV as a notable exception,
ownership among engineers tends to be higher than are the national
averages for the combined well-to-do and middle-class groups (as
indicated by unpublished figures supplied by Social Surveys, Gallup
Poll, 1962). This may be partially because engineers have special
facilities for buying certain items at a discount through their work –
which would indicate another link between work and life style – but,
whatever the explanation, the pattern is one of home owners who are
ardent consumers.

The proportions having various durable goods are: vacuum
cleaner, 94 per cent; radio, 91 per cent; car, 88 per cent; TV, 82 per
cent; washing machine, 79 per cent; refrigerator, 74 per cent; record
player or gramophone, 41 per cent; radiogram, 31 per cent; dish-
washing machine, 3 per cent. One-third own at least five of the items
listed, one-third own six items, and the remaining third have seven or
more.

In terms of the amount of ownership of durables, the economic
style of life of engineers is an affluent one. Home ownership is the

L

major indicator, but the smaller items are equally revealing. While ownership of each item is related to income, even the patterns of ownership among the youngest and most poorly paid engineers are considerably above national middle-class trends. The most discriminating item in its relation to income is the refrigerator, but even this is owned by 62 per cent of those in the lowest income category – and by 92 per cent of those with top incomes. Similarly cars, the largest consumer item apart from a home, are owned by three-quarters of those in the lowest income group and by 97 per cent of those with top incomes.

CONCLUSIONS

The examination of the engineer in his leisure pursuits and attitudes has pointed to some of the connexions between work and non-work roles. A fairly high degree of convergence between the two realms is indicated by the numbers pursuing work-connected hobbies, the extent of work-connected reading, and the frequency of inclusion of colleagues among social contacts. To the extent that all professionals tend to be highly committed to their work, patterns of convergence are to be expected. On the other hand, a preference for pure leisure is very marked on the part of engineers, and is considerably stronger than that found among other occupational groups. Convergence of work and leisure would, accordingly, seem more an actuality than a recognized occupational ideology.

Differences among engineers are considerable. A major factor influencing type of leisure pursued is age, but career variables are equally relevant. In most cases the less successful and the non-graduates are clearly distinguished from the more successful and the graduates. This distinction applies to the home-centred pattern as contrasted with the wider participation in various types of social contact. Types of organizational affiliation are similarly divergent, as are political attitude, brow level, and religious orientation.

The engineers as a group represent a highly affluent segment of the new upper-middle class in Britain. They are middlebrows, moderately active in social contacts and community organizations, politically Conservative with a sizable Liberal streak, not more religious than the nation as a whole, and committed to their work but valuing their leisure even more.

CHAPTER 10

Conclusion and prospect

SUMMARY

What can we deduce from this study of the life cycle of the mechanical engineer and his habitat in Britain? One of the original aims of the survey was to gather data that would serve as guidance in the design of university engineering courses, but the inevitable broadening of the scope of the investigation has resulted in the obtaining of a good deal of general information regarding the anatomy of the mechanical engineering profession in Britain. In addition to studying engineering education and training, we have considered recruitment to the profession and career patterns, and we have also discovered much more about the engineer as an individual – in terms of his family background, general views, and range of interests. Without information of this more personal nature, it is not possible to achieve a full understanding of the educational issues and needs of the profession. What, then, are our general impressions?

It is clear that the engineering profession in Britain has grown up in a different way from many others in that it has developed upwards from the practical craft side and has only more recently become increasingly academic and scientific. Partly as a result of this pattern of development, it is now excessively subdivided into separate specialist institutions. Whether or not these are justifiable from the technical standpoint, this fragmentation of interests and lack of a common professional body constitute one of the main reasons why the public image of engineering as a single profession is blurred and why its status is relatively low in Britain compared with other countries. Another reason is that the charters of the engineering institutions have inhibited their activities in the broadest professional sense, so that they cannot speak as an influential body in the same way as, for instance, the British Medical Association.

In most other countries the engineering profession has a recognized two-tier structure, the top tier consisting of university graduates and the second tier of those who have been trained for a shorter period in technical colleges. In Britain likewise there is, in practice, a similar two-tier structure, but no attempt has been made hitherto to distinguish between the two tiers, and both graduates and non-graduates are included in the same broad class of chartered engineer. This leads to a certain ambiguity of function, and although both groups have the same label, in general they may have quite different responsibilities and receive widely varying financial rewards.

In engineering there is obviously room at the top for all types provided they have ability, and the more loosely-knit system in Britain enables the good man to get to the top whatever his educational status. This is not the case in some countries where once a man is trained for the second tier it is almost impossible for him to get into the top tier. Nevertheless, in the sample studied, the proportion of graduates in the successful group is much higher than that of non-graduates, reflecting the much greater chance the graduate has of attaining a well-paid job.

Engineering in Britain, as in many other countries, appears to be in the forefront of the professions as regards the utilization of the nation's manpower resources, and the social changes that have taken place in Britain have appreciably altered the pattern of recruitment with the result that a much greater proportion than formerly are entering the profession from lower-middle-class and working-class homes. More of these have had a grammar school education, and an increasing percentage are able to go to university or undertake some alternative full-time system of higher education. Although the proportion entering the profession after a full-time higher education may be expected to increase in future, currently the mechanical engineering profession is remarkable for the very low proportion of university graduates that it employs. The relatively low status of the profession in Britain has made it difficult to attract to it sufficient schoolboys of high quality, most of whom prefer science. Moreover, among those who do choose engineering, far more qualify by part-time education than by taking a university degree. The result is that less than a quarter of the members of the Institution of Mechanical Engineers are graduates, and this proportion has not been increasing over the years.

Although family background and type of school attended undoubtedly have an influence, the most important single factor determining success is going to a university. Among university graduates there is a strong correlation between academic ability and subsequent success, which is also related to type of university. This last association is seen most strongly in the case of the Camford honours graduates who are, however, different from other graduates in that most come from professional families and have been to public school.

Most engineers work in commerce and private industry for large organizations, the proportions of graduates and non-graduates being similar for most industries and varying little with age group. The chemical industry employs the highest proportion of graduates, and particularly first-class graduates. The largest employers are the mechanical equipment, electrical and electronic, and chemical and plastics industries. Chances of success are best in the chemical industry, and in general are more favourable in smaller firms where there is greater likelihood of an administrative post.

The variety of work within any particular engineering job is very wide. Most engineers, and especially graduates, seem to spend a large amount of time on office and administrative work. Although relatively few graduates are employed full time on design, most of the sample devote some of their time to design questions and also to research and development.

Most engineers appear to be actively involved in the taking of decisions connected with various aspects of their jobs and organizations. The older ones tend to be in charge of larger groups and the chances of being so are closely related to class of degree.

Consistent with trends in other occupations, it is the older men in managerial posts, especially in small firms, who put in the longest working hours. The younger men work relatively short hours compared with their counterparts overseas.

Whereas the first job of most non-graduates is that of draughtsman, the graduate usually begins as an assistant engineer. He therefore gets a more favourable entrée to the profession and thereafter maintains a better chance of success.

About one-third of mechanical engineers, more than in any other single functional category, are in management, mostly on the technical side. Positions in RD and D and in non-industrial careers are related to the possession of a good honours degree. There are very few graduates, particularly honours graduates, in the important field of design. There is a general exodus from operations and research and development into administration, and by the age of 55 half the profession have attained a managerial position; indeed, if a man has not done so by 55, he is unlikely ever to become a manager. Initial education at university has more effect upon success than has career pattern.

Mobility of engineers between organizations is surprisingly high compared with the findings of other studies, the average mechanical engineer having had seven jobs or promotions by the end of his career. Generally speaking, excessive movement between organizations tends to harm chances of success; but, on the other hand, extreme immobility also tends to negative results. The individual unwilling to make at least one geographical move is unlikely to achieve success where he is.

Job titles broadly correspond with financial success and in all branches graduates earn more than non-graduates. Non-graduates have their best chance of high incomes in managerial posts.

Personal expectations are a function of both actual achievement and possibilities within particular career lines. Hence younger men are more modest in their expectations than older ones. In all groups, as might be anticipated, a much higher proportion expect to get a high income than is warranted by the current distribution of salaries. The only universal theme of anticipation was concerned with reaching a particular level in an organizational hierarchy, thus suggesting that the engineer tends to be an organization man.

The types of school to which engineers wish to send their children are related to their income, attainments, and aspirations, but the desire to send children to university is not related to income, depending rather upon whether the father is a graduate.

A remarkable degree of job satisfaction is implied in the fact that almost one-quarter hope that their sons will become engineers. On the other hand, most engineers are dissatisfied with the status of their profession, and accord it a higher ranking than they know it is accorded by the general public. The vast majority find the work of engineering itself to be their major reward, their main frustration being caused by bad management. Generally, equal proportions of engineers have a technical and an administrative orientation, but the latter increases with length of service and status. The majority are strongly committed to engineering and would choose it again as a career if they had the opportunity.

Only one-fifth take an active part in the activities of their institution, notably the graduates and those in non-industrial posts. Graduates are also more productive of lectures, publications, and inventions. One-fifth read no technical journals and only one in three hundred reads foreign-language periodicals.

Compared with the average Briton, the engineer is remarkable for the small number of hours he spends watching television, the graduates and the successful spending least time in this way. A very high proportion claim work-connected reading as a hobby. Engineers, especially the graduates, the successful, and the managers, lead a fairly active social life, frequently with colleagues, but total involvement in community life is only moderate. Graduates and non-graduates differ, the former being more likely to belong to some voluntary organization and to be more interested in cultural pursuits. The preference of engineers for leisure activities uncontaminated by their work is considerably stronger than that expressed by many other occupational groups.

In their leisure pursuits graduates and non-graduates differ considerably, the honours graduates being distinctive in their tastes, politics, and reading. As a group, engineers represent an affluent section of the new upper-middle class in Britain. They are middle-brows, moderately active in social contacts and community organizations, politically Conservative with a sizable Liberal streak, not more religious than the nation as a whole, devoted to their work, but valuing their leisure even more.

As individuals, therefore, they are remarkably committed to and content with their work, although they realize that the status of their profession is lower than it should be. Perhaps it is their very satisfaction with their work that restrains them as individuals and as a profession from taking more active steps to improve their image and to influence public life.

PROBLEMS

Many of the problems facing the mechanical engineering profession in Britain today are complex, involving not only technical but political and social factors, and their solution is therefore correspondingly difficult. The first step towards progress is to see clearly the nature of the main problems and it is hoped that our survey may have helped in this respect. Broadly speaking, the primary issues are the status of the profession, engineering education, recruitment, and the utilization of skill in practice. These are all interdependent factors and they cannot be dealt with separately; for instance, recruitment and utilization are obviously affected by the status question. In the following review, therefore, which discusses each topic in turn, it must be remembered that the problems are in fact interlinked, as are their solutions.

Status

A basic drawback is the relatively low status of the engineering profession in Britain. Until this is improved it will be difficult to maintain sufficiently high standards of recruitment. As we have seen, Britain contrasts strongly with some Continental countries in this respect, and it seems clear that the lack of status may be partly explained by the current usage of the term 'engineer', which presents a vague image to the general public, and by the multiplicity of the professional engineering institutions. The word engineer conveys such different meanings to different people that it is hard to see how this problem of terminology can be overcome. Putting an adjective such as 'professional' or 'chartered' before 'engineer' will be little help until there is one corporate body of professional or chartered engineers whose function is clearly understood by the public. The existence of at least thirteen separate engineering institutions, each granting its own qualifications, is a handicap to this aspect of public relations.

Further examination reveals that there are many ways of qualifying as a professional engineer in Britain, and that graduates and non-graduates are included under the same professional title. Once again this leads to confusion in the mind of the layman, who at least knows that there is only one way of becoming a doctor or a dentist.

Apart from the fact that the structure of the engineering profession is rather complicated and therefore hard to appreciate, many of the public are ignorant of the true nature of the work and responsibilities of the professional engineer. Whereas the work of the medical profession is readily understood because most of us have had personal experience of it and, in addition, have read books and seen films and television programmes which vividly illustrate its activities, engineering on the other hand is little publicized and, on the rare occasions when it is mentioned in the press or on radio or television, it is often misnamed 'science'. Much therefore remains to be done to explain the work of the engineering profession and to simplify its structure so that it may be more generally understood.

Graduates and non-graduates

One of our primary interests, as the sampling technique indicates, was to compare graduates and non-graduates, and our findings are notable for both the similarities and the differences that they reveal between the two groups.

Although graduates are generally more successful than non-graduates and tend to have different social origins, in both groups there has been an increase of upward mobility. But this does not necessarily imply that all engineers are being used to the best advantage. Both graduates and non-graduates are professional engineers, but are they the same sort of animal, and, indeed, should they be? This question is critical in the light of what is probably the most striking finding, the relatively limited intake of graduates to the profession, which must be considered in relation to many unanswered questions about national priorities for technical manpower. We cannot claim to have isolated all the essential differences between graduates and non-graduates. For instance, are those who achieved the status of graduate simply the better men whose talent would have been revealed whatever their educational experience? Or are they better men because of their experience at university, and, if so, what is it about university training that makes such a difference? Is it the distinctive analytical approach and the greater intensity of the university course? What are the implications for the engineering profession if the proportion of non-graduates continues to increase? What will be the consequences as the Colleges of Advanced Technology become universities and, together with the other new universities, turn out larger proportions of graduate engineers?

Another set of questions relates to class of degree. Where is it that the man with an honours degree or with a first-class degree is most needed? Again, the issue is one of priorities. Is it desirable that only a relatively small number of first-class men should go into industrial posts? What is it about the combination of a good degree and a good university that results in high success-rates? Just as non-graduates appear to be on the increase, so, among the graduates, with the growth of provincial universities, the proportion of Camford men is decreasing, and the implications of this decline must be faced.

What of the large majority of non-graduates? Would the successful have been even more successful if they had been to university, or are they people of outstanding ability who would have climbed their way to the top irrespective of education and social background; or are they in top positions now because of the past shortage of university graduates who, if they had been in greater supply, would have filled these same positions? What will be the chances of the non-graduate in future when a larger proportion of engineers will have been through university? The problem will be to maintain the correct numerical balance between the graduate and the non-graduate streams to satisfy the needs of the profession and of the country.

Engineering education

Related to the basic issue of two different streams producing professional engineers is the question of the content of their education and training. While present courses at universities and elsewhere seem broadly satisfactory in their technical content, they are not creating complete engineers who have any breadth of education either in non-technical fields or even in technical communication. The ability to understand men, like the ability to understand machines, can to a certain extent be learnt on the job, but the task is easier if one has a grasp of the principles beforehand. In this aspect, engineering education is gravely deficient.

Given the universal need for mathematics and the conventional engineering subjects, together with the demand for more liberal studies, it would seem likely that the university course should be a year longer, as has also been recommended by the Robbins Committee (Ministry of Education, 1963*a*). The difficulty in practice is how to give adequate breadth and depth to the course without making it too long and unwieldy. The greatest overall efficiency might be achieved by educating for four or five years those who are capable of benefiting from a high-level university engineering education, even if this means putting the academically less able through a different type of course. Ideally, engineers should return to university after a few years in industry for refresher and advanced courses in old and new subjects. A number of postgraduate courses are now available but they are very poorly supported, largely because the young engineer cannot usually afford to return to university nor is his firm in most cases willing to finance him.

Dissatisfaction with industrial training schemes, which frequently seem deficient in conception and supervision, is symptomatic of the relatively weak ties between industry and educational institutions. Although the sandwich courses developed by the Colleges of Advanced Technology have done much to remedy this situation, there is still room for improvement. After a particularly intensive course at university, many graduate apprentices find their training an anticlimax. Some of the project training schemes may be worth promoting because they have a psychological advantage in that they provide a real challenge for the trainees and also a sense of responsibility. There is a general feeling that works training should be obtained either before or during the period of higher education, rather than after it, which suggests that universities could help by formulating a requirement that industrial training be taken prior to entry, or by making more formal arrangements for such experience during long vacations. A fundamental difficulty, however, with all types of sandwich course, is that responsibility is split between the teaching institution and industry. With the best of goodwill it is difficult to provide a properly integrated course because of the divergent aims and interests of industry and education.

Utilization of skill

The third aspect, closely related to educational issues, is that of the efficient utilization of professional engineers in industry. The similarity in the representation of graduates and non-graduates in various types of work is striking. Yet why is it that in all of these fields the graduates are more successful? Is it just the 'snob' value of a degree, as is sometimes claimed? The large proportion of engineers working in operations, presumably at the expense of research, development, and design, would not seem to indicate the best use of professional training. Furthermore, the general exodus from operations and RD and D into management reveals how short technical ladders appear to be. Certainly management needs good men with technical experience, but the drain on the technical side may be damaging. Also, if there are many administrators who have entered management because they felt blocked and frustrated in their technical work, although their real interests remain on the technical side, then the effect will be detrimental to management too. The most striking evidence suggesting misuse of trained men is that half the respondents feel that parts of their work could be done by individuals who have less technical training, this being especially true in operations and RD and D. This finding indicates again that technical ladders are too short, and also poorly constructed.

On the part of industry, therefore, the first need is for recognition of the engineer as a professional who should be used as such. Although some engineers will, of course, go on to make valuable contributions to management, the professional potential of many can be more fully realized in careers on the technical side. It is wasteful to employ large numbers of either graduates or non-graduates on technical work that does not require their training and skill. This tendency to employ high-grade technical labour on routine work has led to imbalance in the distribution of graduates between large and small firms and between various industries. The natural conservatism and also sometimes the ignorance of small firms have contributed to this situation, and it is desirable that a larger proportion of professional engineers should be employed in the numerous small engineering firms in Britain. It is no accident that the most successful industries are those that employ the highest proportion of graduates.

Membership structure

The mechanical engineering profession may well have to reconsider the criteria and classes of its institution membership in order to conform more closely with the two-tier structure elsewhere. If there is a qualitative difference between university graduates and other engineers, should both groups be included in the same broad class of corporate membership? If there is not a qualitative difference, why the disparate rates of success of the two groups? Faced with the demand for greater numbers of technologists, should we treat them all as graduates? Problems arise whatever system is chosen; for it is essential that the outstanding but relatively unqualified men should be able to get to the top. Should the membership structure be modified to recognize non-graduates as the second tier and, if so, how can this be done equitably?

RECOMMENDATIONS

As we have previously pointed out, the major problems facing the engineering profession form a vicious circle and the difficulty is to decide where it is best to break in. It seems incumbent upon us, nevertheless, having completed our study, to venture a few suggestions. To make a factual survey of the present position is relatively simple and straightforward but to advise useful action on the basis of the information obtained is less easy. In education, for instance, one must look well into the future because of the inevitable time lag entailed, and one has to decide to what extent the present should be allowed to influence one's predictions. Preserving the *status quo* is unlikely to be a valid solution, but neither is an attempt to remedy all the current ills, for only some of these will be pertinent in the future. We must therefore endeavour, in the light of the facts revealed from the survey, to identify significant trends and to anticipate what problems will be facing the engineering industry in perhaps fifteen years' time. Such predictions can be only subjective and tentative, given the nature of the task. The following recommendations are humbly ventured in the hope that some at least may be deemed worthy of discussion and further investigation, and may even be acted upon, for action is essential if the challenge of tomorrow is to be met.

Recruitment

A fundamental need from the national standpoint is to reach and maintain a high level of recruitment, in terms of both quality and quantity, to the engineering profession. This issue is associated with the general question of the status of the profession, and also with the greater national problem of making the best use of the talents available within the country. This, in turn, takes us back to school education, for it is already known that ability to make the grade depends not only upon intelligence but upon environment and family background as well. The intelligent boy from a working-class family stands less chance of success at school than a boy of similar intelligence quotient from a middle-class family. The Newsom Report (Ministry of Education, 1963b) has also drawn attention to disparate educational standards between schools in different neighbourhoods. Despite, therefore, the improved opportunities for education in the 'welfare state', it is clear that the system is still wasteful of the abilities of many basically intelligent children whose potential is not fully developed owing to social and environmental inequalities. Much, therefore, needs to be done on a national scale to ensure that all children of ability have equal opportunity to better themselves.

As we have seen, similar considerations apply to the higher education of recruits to the engineering profession, where it seems that at the moment the dice are loaded against the intelligent boy from a relatively poor family. Although he has an outside chance of success, his prospects would be greatly enhanced if he could get to university rather than qualify by part-time education. Current social and educational changes may help to remedy this situation, but it is essential for the nation's economy and for the wellbeing of the engineering profession that intelligent and able recruits of humble social background should be given every chance to progress. The country cannot afford to waste such people and much will depend in future upon what proportion of school-leavers go on to university and what proportion to some other kind of full-time higher education, and on how industrial firms encourage and train both groups.

Assessment of technical manpower needs

The Robbins Committee on higher education (Ministry of Education, 1963*a*) certainly pointed out the need to provide more university places for school-leavers, but it intentionally sidestepped the question of deciding on priorities between the various disciplines. The committee did, in fact, recommend a slight increase in places in technology compared with pure science, but it made no attempt to prescribe the appropriate balance between science, arts, medicine, economics, and the social sciences. A *laissez-faire* attitude towards the university situation may be in the true democratic tradition; it is hardly likely to be in the national interest, which would be best served if guidance and controls were exercised to encourage entry into those disciplines in which the need for trained people is most urgent. This whole question is delicate and complex, but it would appear imperative to appoint a high-level body with the responsibility of deciding, on the basis of reliable economic data and up-to-date manpower statistics, the country's needs in terms of manpower, at all levels of ability, for the occupations essential to its wellbeing. It may be argued that this is an impossible task, but some other countries are already attempting periodic assessments along these lines in order to determine their educational and economic priorities. In Britain the first steps must be to establish and maintain the recording of comprehensive statistics in the area of technical manpower – which are at present sadly lacking – and to undertake regular surveys of the position. Manpower requirements could then be assessed systematically in the light of economic needs in close collaboration with the National Economic Development Council, the Committee for Scientific and Technological Manpower, and other relevant bodies.

The engineering profession is, of course, competing with other professions for manpower, but it must get its appropriate share of the talent available and be quite clear about what proportions of graduates, non-graduates, technologists, and technicians it requires to meet anticipated production and export programmes.

Considerations of status

A factor that militates against recruitment to the engineering profession is the lack of glamour and poor publicity that it is accorded in comparison with pure science. The result is that to a school-leaver the stereotype of the scientist is much more attractive than that of the engineer, and there is, in addition, a widespread feeling that, intellectually, engineering is a low-grade activity suitable for boys who are not very good at mathematics or physics. This impression is not corrected by schoolmasters who are themselves pure scientists, and therefore uninformed about engineering as a career. More school-leavers of high ability must be attracted towards the engineering profession, which means that the public image of the profession must be improved. It falls to the engineering institutions to convince the public of the critical importance of the engineering contribution. The institutions have not been very active in this respect but are now beginning to wake up to the needs of the situation. They and the universities are now trying, by means of booklets, films, and talks, to give parents and schoolmasters a better idea of what engineering involves and to emphasize the high standard of all-round ability that is required to make a successful engineer. There are also signs that, following the lead given by the Minister for Science, the press, radio, and television are beginning to take a more intelligent interest in the engineering profession and they have recently produced material which may convey to the public a greater awareness of the industry's role and a realistic appreciation of the nature of engineering work. Much more can be done by means of the mass communication media, and engineers themselves must be energetic and articulate if they are to rouse interest and enthusiasm in their work. It may take some time to improve the public image, but success in this respect would undoubtedly be highly beneficial.

A factor that can be used to raise the status of the profession is the persisting shortage of engineers, as forecast by the Committee on Scientific and Technical Manpower (Advisory Council on Scientific Policy, 1963). When engineers are in short supply, their essential contribution to the nation's economy may be emphasized, their salaries may increase because demand exceeds supply, and an indirect result of their scarcity value may be the enhancement of the status of the profession. The shortage of technical manpower and the 'brain drain' have already become subjects of political debate and if they are exploited as important issues in political campaigns the public will undoubtedly be impressed. There are, of course, associated dangers in that engineering, like education, may become a useful political talking-point without anything being done in practice to remedy the situation.

A necessary step towards the achievement of higher status is the establishment of a unified body to replace the multiplicity of institutions now extant and to represent all aspects of the engineering profession. A move has been made in this direction by the formation of the Engineering Institutions' Council (now the CEI, see App. 4), but, unfortunately, the activities of this body are confined to such questions as common qualifying examinations, and do not include wider professional matters such as conditions of work, pensions, and salaries. These are still left to the small but active Engineers' Guild which has agreed quite amicably with the Council to go its separate way for the time being. The sooner an effective joint organization is set up not only to act as a qualifying body but to deal with all matters affecting the profession and to speak with authority on its behalf, the sooner will the status of the profession be improved.

The situation derives urgency in the face of the establishment of the European Common Market and Britain's possible participation therein. On the Continent the engineering societies of various countries (FEANI) have already been working towards common professional standards and reciprocal arrangements to allow registered engineers to practise anywhere in Europe. At the moment, British standards for qualification as a professional engineer differ considerably from those of most other countries, and it will be necessary to examine realistically the implications of this state of affairs and to decide whether registration is desirable and practicable.

Balance between graduates and non-graduates

We have already underlined that opportunities must be such that the outstanding non-graduate is able to get to the top of the profession; nevertheless, it is questionable whether it should be almost a general rule that non-graduates of average ability have the same grade of membership as graduates. Although, as we have seen, graduates and non-graduates do the same type of work in practice, the graduates are on the whole much more successful. Despite their noteworthy success, however, there are relatively few graduates in the mechanical engineering profession, mainly because large numbers of non-graduates qualify by part-time education. In this respect mechanical engineering contrasts strongly with other engineering institutions in Britain, in which the majority of members are graduates. The difference is so marked as to raise the question whether the mechanical engineering industry is radically different from, say, civil or electrical engineering. In practice, there would seem to be no such distinction and we are left with the impression that the present situation is a consequence of the kind of philosophy that obtains about what constitutes a professional engineer. If a system that lays down that all professional engineers must be graduates represents one extreme, then perhaps the mechanical engineering profession, in which only 22 per cent are graduates, is a little too near the other extreme in an age when academic standards must, if anything, rise to keep pace with rapid developments in technology. It is a matter of maintaining a reasonable balance between graduates and non-graduates, and allowing for the fact that there will be some non-graduates who will be top-class engineers and some graduates who will be mediocre.

Ideally, the professional engineer should have both high academic qualifications and extensive works training and practical experience. Perhaps a more realistic appraisal of the work functions and responsibilities of the main types of professional engineer would help towards a clearer conception of the various levels of skill, for it is becoming increasingly difficult to distinguish between low-grade technologists and high-grade technicians. Outstanding professional engineers are self-evident; the difficulty is to know how to evaluate the others. The present expansion of the universities and the tendency towards full-time technical education may help to make standards more uniform, but, again, part-time facilities must be available to enable talented individuals who cannot get to university or college to enter the engineering profession.

Specification of educational aims
On the question of engineering education, there must be fairly general agreement as to the ultimate aims of the education process and some means of determining the right balance between quality and quantity. As we have seen, engineering work requires many types

M

of people and a wide range of abilities, and it would be helpful if the qualifying bodies, the institutions, and industry could agree on what proportions of each type will be needed. In the face of the current shortage of engineers, it is essential to make the best use of those already available. Thus the number of highly qualified senior engineers, who create and initiate projects, must be weighed against the numbers of various levels of ancillary staff, who are required to see projects through to the marketing stage. The relative needs of various industries, of public companies, educational establishments, consulting firms, and so on will have to be borne in mind. The demand for engineers must be estimated not only in respect of numbers but also in terms of quality and type of skill, so that it can be related to education and training. For instance, honours engineering courses at universities primarily educate undergraduates for research posts or for teaching, and as a result many go into such occupations. If honours-type minds are required for other kinds of work, should these courses be modified in some way? There is some confusion of aims among the Colleges of Advanced Technology (see App. 4), which were originally set up to train technologists, people with a specialist knowledge of a particular process or branch of engineering. As they have developed they have evolved courses very similar to those offered by universities, giving a fundamental grounding in engineering subjects but not specialist detailed knowledge of any particular technology. Now that these colleges are becoming universities, will they continue to follow the pattern of the established universities? It may or may not be a good thing if they do so; what is important is to decide on the aims of the particular educational system and to work consistently towards these. There will always be a need for engineers with lower levels of training, and there has to be an adequate supply of well-trained technicians also. The training of technicians has recently been the subject of a government inquiry, and it is undoubtedly closely related to the question of training engineers.

As new universities are established in Britain, the graduate engineer will become the norm, and a task of increasing importance will be the maintenance of uniformly high academic standards. There is evidence that the standards of first-class honours degrees vary considerably between universities, and it will be unfortunate if greater variations are permitted to develop. It seems that academic ability is a good index of future potential as an engineer; thus it is essential both to maintain high standards and to distinguish clearly between outstanding, average, and mediocre talent. There must be no illusions about the relative abilities of the increasing numbers of engineers who will in future be entering the graduate class.

Content and length of training

There was general agreement among respondents that engineering courses should be broader and that, in addition to covering the conventional mathematical and engineering subjects, they should give more time to the field of communication, both writing and drawing, which was a basic function in the engineer's daily work. It was also the feeling that as much as a third of a university engineering course should be devoted to English, writing, and foreign languages, and to industrial administration, economics, and social science. These recommendations for a more liberal course are remarkably similar to others made in America and on the Continent, and are consistent with proposals for the broadening of school education in Britain, as put forward in *The Complete Scientist* (British Association, 1961). If changes are made along these lines, care must be taken to ensure that they do not result in a lowering of the high standards demanded in technical subjects. It is unlikely that the recommended breadth and depth can be achieved without an increase in the length of the course; and since in nearly every other country in the world engineering education occupies at least five or six years, it is time that Britain considered taking a step in the direction of longer courses.

Changes in higher education are inevitably linked with the design of school education. Similar recommendations have been made about broadening the last three years of school education in Britain when, according to the usual pattern, courses lead to a commendably high standard in three subjects, but are specialized and therefore narrow. Specialization at this stage is one of the reasons why university courses tend to be shorter in Britain in comparison with other countries, because the academic qualifications of school-leavers are often a year ahead of those of their counterparts elsewhere and they therefore need a year less at university. It is important to remember, however, that education is narrower in Britain compared with other countries for both the school-leaver and the university student and that, even though the British student may be a year ahead when he enters a university engineering course, by the time of graduation his counterparts in other countries will have received at least one extra year of advanced technical education. By some means, therefore, another year must be found for the technical education of the British engineer – either by rearranging the six-year period at present divided equally between school and university, or by adding a seventh year. It might be practicable to have a strictly two-year course for sixth-formers followed by four years at university. The value of a third year in the sixth form for the would-be engineer is debatable and he might profit by spending the extra time at university or in industry. As far as engineering training is concerned, closer integration between the latter years of school education and the course would help towards the achievement of the two aims of broadening the field of study and maintaining high standards in engineering subjects.

Integration of academic and practical training
At the same time, it is desirable to include works training within the period of education and training, which would thus extend, in the case of those who became university graduates, for about seven years from the age of 16. Although the sample studied expressed general satisfaction with their college and university education, they were much less satisfied with their experience of industrial training. There is obviously scope for improved schemes integrating academic education and practical training. Moreover, since nearly everyone felt that practical training should preferably be prior to or during the period of academic education, some, at least, of the works training should take place before entry to university, and the remainder should be done during the university course. In some countries it is already a requirement that engineering students must have spent some time in recognized industrial training before they are allowed to enter university: Germany and Norway specify six months and a year, respectively. In these countries the state supervises the industrial training to ensure that it is satisfactory; in Britain supervision would present more of a problem because the engineering institutions, and not the state, are at present responsible. Universities may also need to make more formal arrangements for the works training of their students during vacations.

Trainee engineers who are not going to university need an equally well-designed system of theoretical and practical education, and as precise a scale of rewards for their qualifications as is offered to graduates. At present there is insufficient encouragement from firms in this respect, and thus in many cases the trainees lack incentive because they know that even if they pass their examinations they are unlikely to get more money as a result.

It has in the past been argued that owing to the shortage of teachers and of university and college places, Britain cannot afford to increase the length of engineering education and training. But the acceptance of such a view may well be false economy, and the country ought to contemplate very seriously the dangers inherent in a skimping of technical education at all levels. The fact that other countries can apparently afford a longer training for engineers may eventually put Britain at a disadvantage in an age of fierce competition and rapidly developing technology, when engineers must be highly equipped if they are to cope with the exacting problems they are likely to encounter.

Skill and career prospects

There is a general need for the more efficient utilization of the engineer on work for which he was trained and in which he is interested. This aspect is closely linked with the question of the status of the engineer in his firm *vis-à-vis* other professional and managerial staff, and with relative career prospects on the technical and the managerial side. At present, purely technical career prospects are not so favourable, with the result that the majority of older engineers become managerial. This may be a good thing if they are genuinely interested in management, but danger lies in the drift from the technical side. The solution of this problem will require a fuller appreciation by management of the functions and capabilities of engineers. There was a general feeling among respondents that some aspects of their work could be handled by individuals with less technical training and supportive evidence for the criticism that both graduate and non-graduate engineers are underemployed on technical work. The aim should be to relieve engineers of some of the routine office work that occupies much of their time and to use them more intensively on technical problems.

It is probable that, by having more engineers at board level, firms could increase their understanding of engineering work and be more successful in their employment of engineers. Is it true, for instance, that the average engineer has outlived his usefulness on purely technical work by the age of 45–50? If so, what is to be done with him? Is it reasonable to transfer him to managerial work, and what additional training will he require? It is undesirable, obviously, for engineers to be driven into administration because they are frustrated on the technical side. Managements must provide adequate career prospects for good people on the technical side, so that those who transfer to managerial posts do so because they are generally interested in administration. It is managements' duty to get the best out of their staff and it may be that there are not enough well-qualified people at the top, for one of the major frustrations of engineers seems to be poor management.

Distribution of engineers

The overall distribution of engineers within industry should be critically examined. There are not enough engineers, for instance, with small firms which might benefit considerably from expert assistance. There are too few graduates, and particularly honours graduates, in the basic field of design. The technical and economic value of good design and good designers has been underestimated by management and steps are now being taken to alter this situation as a result of the inquiry and recommendations of the Feilden Committee (DSIR, 1963). Furthermore, the distribution of honours graduates, particularly first-class men, is not sufficiently even. More should be encouraged to find their way to the operations side. In general, the balance of engineers between research and operations may need adjustment, for, compared with the United States, in Britain relatively few full-time staff are devoted to research and development, although it must be admitted that many seem to spend part of their time on work in these areas. Once again, it is a question of securing the distributions of staff and time that yield the best results.

There is no doubt that Britain will depend more and more in future upon the skill of its engineers if the country is to earn its way in the world. Modern society is largely dependent upon the engineering industry for the provision of the services and consumer and capital goods that have become essential to the twentieth-century way of life. The pressures of automation are already being exerted; old methods of engineering practice and education must give way to new; and a new and vigorous management must arise, equipped to meet the challenge of complex technical and social problems thrown up in an age of rapid technological change.

Questionnaire

<table>
<tr><td rowspan="2">Private
and
Confi-
dential</td><td>SOCIAL SURVEYS (GALLUP POLL) LTD – CS 4165 – JAN./FEB. 1962</td><td></td><td></td><td></td></tr>
<tr><td>Time started.........a.m./p.m.</td><td>Reporter's
No.</td><td>Ser.
No.</td><td></td></tr>
</table>

It is of the utmost importance to ask the questions exactly as they are worded on the form.
Do not read out answers.

First of all, we would like some information about your educational background.

1 What type of school Elementary 1
did you last attend? Secondary technical 2
Secondary modern; Junior secondary 3
Grammar; Senior secondary; Academy 4
Public (private) or Independent day 5
Public (private) or Independent boarding........... 6
Other (*write in*) ....

2 Could you tell me the full name of the school?

....

3(a) At what age did you leave there? ....

(b) At school did you do anything like engineering, metalwork, electrical or
radio work, either as a school subject or as a hobby, which aroused or
increased your interest in engineering?
School subjects:
Academic – e.g. maths, physics, etc. 1
Engineering subjects 2
Other practical subjects 3
Hobbies or other activities (*write in*)

....
....
....

None at school... V

173

4   What school-leaving or higher examinations did you pass at school? In what subjects? (*Mark all subjects for each exam passed.*)

	School-leaving certificate, GSC, GCE 'O' level, Matric	Higher school certificate, Inter., GCE 'A' level	Ordinary national
English	1	1	1
Latin, Greek	2	2	2
Modern languages	3	3	3
Maths: pure, applied	4	4	4
Physics, chemistry	5	5	5
Botany, zoology, biology	6	6	6
History, geography, economics	7	7	7
Art, music	8	8	8
Metalwork, woodwork	9	9	9
Other (*write in*)			
....	0	0	0
....	X	X	X
....			

5(a) Which degrees, diplomas, certificates and Institution examinations have you completed? (*Mark in grid below.*)

   Ask for each one completed:
(b) What year did you attain............?

(c) At which college or university did you study for it?

(d) Which years were you there?

(a) Degree, diploma, certificates		(b) Year attained	(c) College or university	(d) Years attended
Institution exam.	1	....	....	....
University degree	2	....	....	....
Dip. Tech.	3	....	....	....
Associateship & Diploma	4	....	....	....
Higher National Diploma	5	....	....	....
Higher National Certificate with endorsement	6	....	....	....
Other (*write in*)				

5(e) *If university degree:*
    What class was your degree?

	Internal	External
First	1	 7
Second undivided	2	 8
Upper second	3	 9
Lower second	4	 0
Third	5	 X
Pass	6	 V

Other (*write in*) ....

Ask all:

6(a) How did you obtain your engi-   Full-time 1
neering qualifications – full-time   Part-time day 2
or part-time courses, evening   evening 3
courses, sandwich courses, or   Sandwich 4
by correspondence? (*Mark all*   Correspondence 5
mentioned.)   Other (*write in*)

....

....

If not university, Q. 6(b): (others, skip to Q. 7)

(b) Did you at any time want to go   Yes, for engineering .... O
up to university for a degree in   Yes, for other degree X
engineering or anything else?   No V

(c) What were the circumstances in which you did not (wish to) go to a
university?
....
....

(d) How far has the fact that you have not got a university degree made any
difference to your career?

    A lot of difference 1
    A little difference 2
    No difference 3

(e) *If a difference:* In what ways?
....
....

(f) Do you regret the fact that you   Yes, very much .... O
have not been to university?   Yes, a little X
    No, not at all V

Ask all:

7 Were you trained in Mechanical Engineering only or in some other branches of engineering also? (*Mark all mentioned.*)

Mechanical only	1
Also Civil	2
Electrical	3
Marine	4
Chemical	5
Aeronautical	6
Automobile	7

Other (*write in*) ....
....

8(a) Did you study any subjects in (college) (university) other than science or engineering? If so, what were the subjects? (*Mark or write in below.*)

(b) How long did you study (*each*)?

	Q. 8(a)	Q. 8(b) Length of study			
		Less than one year	One year	Two years	Three years and more
English	1	1	2	3	4
Modern languages	2	5	6	7	8
Economics – general principles	3	9	0	X	V
– applied, e.g. costing etc.	4	1	2	3	4
Industrial administration, Industrial relations (*write in details*)					
....		5	6	7	8
....		9	0	X	V
Other (*write in*)					
....		1	2	3	4
....		5	6	7	8

No non-engineering subjects studied V

9(a) For each subject on this card (*show card A*) would you tell me whether you have found it to be essential in your work, very useful, moderately useful, or of little or no use in your work?

(b) If you never formally studied any of these subjects, please mention this when we come to it. (*Interviewer: for subjects not formally studied, ring degree of use and never studied. Ask Q. 9(a) first, for all subjects, then continue with Q. 9(c).*)

(c) How many times have you used (*each subject*) within the past five working days?

	An answer must be marked for each subject (a)				Also mark if applicable (b)	No. of times used in past five working days (c)		
	Essential	Very useful	Mod. use	No use	Never formally studied	Not used	Once	More than once
Maths	1	1	1	1	1	1	1	1
Applied mechanics	2	2	2	2	2	2	2	2
Statistics	3	3	3	3	3	3	3	3
Heat, light, and sound	4	4	4	4	4	4	4	4
Principles of electricity	5	5	5	5	5	5	5	5
Electrotechnology (including electronics)	6	6	6	6	6	6	6	6
Engineering drawing	7	7	7	7	7	7	7	7
Production engineering	8	8	8	8	8	8	8	8
Work study	9	9	9	9	9	9	9	9
Industrial administration and economics	X	X	X	X	X	X	X	X
Foreign languages	V	V	V	V	V	V	V	V
Technical report writing	1	1	1	1	1	1	1	1
Properties and strength of materials	2	2	2	2	2	2	2	2
Metallurgy	3	3	3	3	3	3	3	3
Theory of structures	4	4	4	4	4	4	4	4
Theory of machines	5	5	5	5	5	5	5	5
Automatic control, instrumentation, and servo-mechanism	6	6	6	6	6	6	6	6
Vibration	7	7	7	7	7	7	7	7
Thermodynamics	8	8	8	8	8	8	8	8
Mechanics of fluids and hydraulics	9	9	9	9	9	9	9	9
Heat engines (internal combustion, steam, refrigeration)	X	X	X	X	X	X	X	X
Fuel and combustion engineering	V	V	V	V	V	V	V	V

9 (d) Did you study any additional speciality subjects, e.g. aeronautical engineering, automotive engineering, textile engineering? If so, have you found them to be essential, very useful, moderately useful, or not useful in your work?

(e) How many times have you used (*each subject*) within the past five working days? Speciality subjects (*write in*)

	Essen-tial	Very useful	Mod. useful	No use	No. of times used in past five working days		
					Not used	Once	More than once
.... ☐	3	4	5	6	0	1	2
.... ☐	3	4	5	6	0	1	2
.... ☐	3	4	5	6	0	1	2

No speciality subjects studied...............V

10 What percentage of time, if any, would you recommend should be devoted to each of the areas on this card in an engineering degree course? (*The total should be 100%; show card B.*)
Please give your answer to the nearest 5%

	Percentage of time on degree course
English and humanities	....
Technical report writing	....
Foreign languages	....
Industrial administration, economics, and social sciences	....
Fundamental sciences, e.g. maths, physics, chemistry	....
Basic engineering sciences, e.g. strength of materials	....
Design engineering	....
Speciality engineering, excluding design, e.g. instrument engineering or textiles	....
Total	100%

11 If you could have your education over again, are there any additional engineering or non-engineering subjects you missed out, which you would now study? Which ones? At what stage?

Engineering subjects	Non-engineering subjects
(a) At school	(a) At school
.... ☐	.... ☐
.... ☐	.... ☐
(b) Higher education	(b) Higher education
.... ☐	.... ☐
.... ☐	.... ☐
None............V	None............V

12 Which of the objectives listed on this card would you rank 1st, 2nd, 3rd, and 4th in an ideal engineering course? (*Show card C.*)

	1st	2nd	3rd	4th
To teach specific skills, e.g. drawing, design, engine tests, etc.	1	2	3	4
To teach students the technique of scientific method and to stimulate them to think about their subject	5	6	7	8
To teach the fundamentals of the main subjects: applied mechanics, fluid mechanics, thermodynamics, etc.	9	O	X	V
To teach special branches of engineering, e.g. automotive and power engineering	10	20	30	40

13 A recent survey by the Engineers' Guild showed that, among professional engineers, university graduates earn more than non-graduates. What do you think are the reasons for this difference in earnings? (*Write in as fully as possible. If vague answers, e.g. 'They are better', ask 'Why?' or 'Would you explain more fully?'*)

....

....

.... ☐☐

14(a) How adequate do you think engineering education is in British universities today?

| Very adequate .... 1 |
| Fairly adequate .... 2 |
| Not very adequate .... 3 |
| Not at all adequate.................... 4 |

Other (*write in*) 5

(b) Why do you say this? (*Write in.*)

....

....

....

15(a) What about the engineering education at technical colleges? How adequate is that?

Very adequate 7
Fairly adequate 8
Not very adequate 9
Not at all adequate......................... 0

Other (*write in*).. X

(b) Why do you say this? (*Write in.*)

....
.... ☐☐

16(a) Should industrial works experience ideally be obtained before, during or after academic education?

Before 1
During 2
After 3

Other (*write in*) ....

(b) Why do you say this? (*Write in.*)

....
....
.... ☐☐

(c) When did you in fact obtain your industrial works experience?

Before academic education 5
During academic education.............. 6
After academic education 7

(d) How long was your formal apprenticeship?

Two-year graduate apprenticeship .... O
Five-year apprenticeship X

Other (*write in*) ....

17 Was the best possible use made of the time you spent on your apprenticeship?
If no: How could it have been improved?

Yes, best use made 1

No (*write in details*)

....
....
....

18 When you first thought of becoming an engineer, did you anticipate going into a management position eventually or did you want to stay on the engineering side?

Management 1
Engineering 2
Combination of both 3
Don't know/didn't think
    about it 4

19   At what age did you first decide to become an engineer? ....

20(a) What were the major factors in your choice?

	First mention	Other mentions
Father or immediate relative in engineering	1	1
Other relatives, friends in engineering	2	2
Influence of parents, relatives who were *not* in engineering	3	3
School influences, teachers, etc.	4	4
Mechanically-minded, good with hands...........................	5	5
Academic aptitude; good at physics, science	6	6
Local industry offered good opportunities	7	7
Only opening available at time..	8	8
Good prospects for career..	9	9
Other (*write in*)		

(b) Was engineering really what you wanted to do at that time or would you rather have done something else? If so, what?

Yes, wanted to do engineering..................... 1

No, would have preferred

....

....

Don't know V

(c) What was your father's major occupation (*or the person mainly responsible for your upbringing*)? *If he was an engineer:* Was he a chartered engineer?

Job ....

Grade ....

Industry ....

(d) *If married:* What was your father-in-law's major occupation? *If he was an engineer:* Was he a chartered engineer?

Job ....

Grade ....

Industry ....

(e) Did you have any (*other*) relatives or close friends in engineering at the time you decided to become an engineer?

Yes

Relatives .... O

Friends X

No, none V

	1st job, etc.

21   What was your first full-time position? What was your job title? (*Write in.*)

22 What type(s) of work did you do mainly? (*Show card D.*)		
	Engineering apprenticeship	.. 1 ..
	Other apprenticeship	.. 2 ..
	Construction	.. 3 ..
	Production/operation	.. 4 ..
	Maintenance	.. 5 ..
	Testing and inspection	.. 6 ..
	Design	.. 7 ..
	Research & development	.. 8 ..
	Work study & operations research	.. 9 ..
	Sales	.. X ..
	Costing & finance	.. V ..
	Administration: Technical	.. 10 ..
	Non-technical	.. 20 ..
	Teaching	.. 30 ..
	Training apprentices	.. 40 ..
	Other (*write in*)	

23(a)   Who were you working for then? (*Write in.*)   ....

....

(b) What size was the firm or branch where you yourself worked?			
	Small	Under 100	.. 1 ..
	Medium	100–499	.. 2 ..
	Large	500 & over	.. 3 ..

(c) And what type of organization was it? (*Show card E.*)		
	Nationalized industry	.. 4 ..
	U.K. Atomic Energy Authority	.. 5 ..
	Public utility undertaking or local authority (excl. teaching)	.. 6 ..
	Commerce & industry	.. 7 ..
	Civil service	.. 8 ..
	University or Technical College	.. 9 ..
	Consulting engineering	.. X ..
	Other (*write in*)	

24   In what locality were you working in this job? (*Write in town or county.*)

25 What year did you get this position and when did you leave it?		
	Obtained	....
	Left	....
	Still there	X

26 What did your new job or position offer that you were not getting in the previous one? (*Mark all mentioned.*)		
	Promotion	.. 1 ..
	Nature of work:	
	prefer administration	.. 2 ..
	prefer technical work	.. 3 ..
	Better immediate salary	.. 4 ..
	In the long run will have better status	.. 5 ..
	In the long run will have better salary	.. 6 ..
	Less technical competition	.. 7 ..
	Better working conditions	.. 8 ..
	Better working associates	.. 9 ..
	Called up for services	.. X ..
	Demobbed, released from services	.. V ..
	Other (*write in*)	

27   What was your next position? (*Mark answer at top of next column and repeat Qs. 22–26 for each job held – including different positions in the same firm – up to and including present position. All years from first job to present date must be accounted for, including war years and national service and years spent on further education or training.*)

28   *If now in administration rather than technical engineering:*
      What was your income in the last technical job you had? (*Show card F.*)
                (*Write in code.*) ....

      Ask all:

29(a) What type of industry are you working in now?

           Construction (*Builders, etc.*) 1
           Extraction (*Coal, oil, mineral*)........................... 2
           Manufacturing – Aircraft 3
                     Automobile 4
                     Shipbuilding 5
                     Railways 6
                     Chemical, plastics and
                          allied..................................... 7
                     Electrical 8
                     Electronic and radio 9
                     Metal production X
                     Materials, paper, bricks,
                          glass, textiles, leather V
                     Mechanical equipment 10

      Other (*write in*) ....
      Not applicable, teaching, etc. (*skip to Q. 30*)   50

    (b) Which production process best describes your industry? (*Read out.*)
                     Unit production 60
                     Small-batch production 70
                     Large-batch or mass production 80
                     Process production 90
      Other (*write in*) ....

30(a) Since you became professionally qualified and completed your apprenticeship, have you done any manual work in any of your jobs for as much as three days at a time?
                     Yes, often 1
                     Yes, occasionally 2
                     No, never 3

    (b) What is your attitude on this point? Do you think it is a good thing to work alongside the men, or is it advisable not to do so in order to maintain one's status?
                     Good thing to work alongside men 5
                     Advisable not to do so 6
      Other answers (*write in*) ....

N

31(a) At present in your job, what proportion of your time do you spend on each type of work – to the nearest 5% in each case? (*Answers must equal 100%; show card G.*)

(b) How far do you, yourself, take decisions or join in the discussions on which decisions are based, for each type of work you do? (*Ask in turn for each item mentioned in Q. 31(a).*)

	% time	Take decisions	Advise or take part in discussions	Take no part at all
Construction	3	3	3	3
Production/operation	4	4	4	4
Maintenance	5	5	5	5
Testing and inspection	6	6	6	6
Design	7	7	7	7
Research and development	8	8	8	8
Work study and operations research	9	9	9	9
Sales	0	0	0	0
Costing and finance	X	X	X	X
Administration:				
Technical	V	V	V	V
Non-technical	10	10	10	10
Routine office work	20	20	20	20
Teaching	30	30	30	30
Training apprentices	40	40	40	40
Other (*write in*)		50	50	50

(c) How about . . . (*ask for each in turn*)?
How far do you, yourself, take decisions or join in the discussions on which decisions are based, for . . . ?
Engagement of

qualified engineers	70	70	70
office staff	80	80	80
factory personnel	90	90	90
Purchase orders of £100 or more	X0	X0	X0
Not applicable, lecturer, own business, consultant engineer	V0		

32(a) Do you think that any of the work you are doing should be done by someone with less technical training so as to give you more time for more
senior work?
If so, which aspects of your work do you have in mind that should be
done by someone else?

Yes, routine clerical work 1
Yes, administrative – non-technical 2
Yes, simple technical work 3

Other (*write in*) ....

No, shouldn't be done by anyone
else V

(b) Do you have a private secretary or not?

Yes, working for me only 1
Share with one or two others 2
No 3

33 Is the whole firm situated where you
work, or is it just one of their fac-
tories, offices, or departments?

Whole firm 5
Not whole firm 6

34(a) How many employees (*technical or otherwise*) are directly in your charge?
(*Write number in box.*)
If don't know: What's your nearest guess? ☐

(b) About how many qualified engineers or scientists are employed altogether
at your particular place of work, including yourself? ☐

35(a) About how many qualified engineers or scientists do you work with
directly? ☐

(b) How many of these are senior to you, how many
are level with you, and how many are junior to   Senior ☐
you?   Level ☐
(*Total should agree with figure in Q. 35(a).*)   Junior ☐

36(a) What is the basic number of hours you work each week at your place of
work without overtime?

.... hours per week

No standard hours (*write in details*)

....
....

36(b) Do you frequently put in extra hours evening and weekends?
If yes: How many extra hours a week would be average?

Yes (*write in no.*) ....
No, rarely or not at all V
Qualified answers
    (*write in*) ....
....

37(a) What was your total earned income, including bonuses, and before tax and other deductions (*show card F*), in the financial year 1960–1961?

Under £1,000 1
£1,000–1,199 2
£1,200–1,399 3
£1,400–1,599 4
£1,600–1,799 5
£1,800–2,199 6
£2,200–2,999 7
£3,000–3,999 8
£4,000–5,999 9
£6,000 and over 0

(b) Are you in any pension scheme operated by your employer or isn't there such a scheme?

Yes, in contributory scheme 1
Yes, in non-contributory
    scheme 2
No, not in scheme 3
No pension scheme.......................... 4
Self-employed 5

38 Have you any general plans or goals for your future career? If so, could you tell me about them?
(*Write in.*)...
....
....
Already at the top of my profession (*skip to Q. 41(a)*) V

39(a) *If job or rank not given:* What do you expect will be the best position you will ever hold?
.... □

(b) Might that be with your present employer or not?

Present employer................................ 1
Other employer 2
Self-employed now 3
Will be self-employed 4
Don't know 5

40(a) How long do you expect to remain in your present position? (*Indicate below.*)

(b) How long do you expect to remain with your present employer? (*Mark below even if same as (a).*)

	(a) In present position	(b) With present employer
Up to 1 year	1	1
Over 1 year–3 years	2	2
Over 3 years–5 years	3	3
Over 5 years–10 years	4	4
Over 10 years	5	5
Until I retire	6	6
Until something better turns up	7	7
Don't know; depends on external circumstances (*in firm or industry*)	8	8
Other (*write in*)	9	
		9

Ask all:

41(a) Assuming the pay would be the same, would you prefer an administrative position or a primarily technical advisory position?
Other (*write in*)

Administrative 1
Technical advisory 2
Combination of both 3
Either, don't mind 4

(b) Why would you prefer that? (*Write in.*)

42 Just as a guess, what would you expect your highest income in any one year in your lifetime to be in terms of present values?

Under £1,000	1	£2,200–2,999	7
£1,000–1,199	2	£3,000–3,999	8
£1,200–1,399	3	£4,000–5,999	9
£1,400–1,599	4	£6,000–9,999	0
£1,600–1,799	5	£10,000 and over	X
£1,800–2,199	6		

43(a) If you had to do it over again, would you stay in engineering or might you choose a different career?

Yes, stay in engineering
definitely 1
probably 2
No, choose a different career
probably 3
definitely 4

(b) *If yes:*
Would you stay in mechanical engineering?

Yes, stay in mechanical
engineering 5
No, choose a different
branch 6

(c) *If no to either Q. 43(a) or (b):*
What career/branch would you choose? (*Write in.*)

....

Ask all:
44(a) What are the major frustrations or dissatisfactions of your work? (*Write in.*)

....
.... □□

(b) What are the major satisfactions of your work? (*Write in.*)

....
.... □□

45 Do you think your previous occupational career has ideally fitted you for your present job or would you rather have come up by some other way? *If any other way:* What other way?

(*Write in.*)   Previous career ideal 1

....
....

46(a) Would you rank each of the occupations on this card on the basis of how much social prestige you *personally* feel these occupations have? (*Show card H.*) Rank 1 = most social prestige, Rank 10 = least social prestige. Which would you rank 1st, 2nd, etc. (*Try not to rank any two the same; continue until all 10 are ranked.*)

(b) Do you think that *people in general* would rate these occupations in any different order or not?
If yes: Would you rate them again as you think the general public would do it?

	(a) Personal ranking	(b) General public ranking
Primary school teacher	....	....
Dentist	....	....
Company director	....	....
University lecturer	....	....
Research physicist	....	....
Professional engineer	....	....
Solicitor	....	....
Works manager	....	....
Doctor	....	....
Chartered accountant	....	....
General public would rank them in the same way		V

47 Why did you rank the engineer as you did?
If '*should be higher*': Why? What do you have in mind? (*Write in.*)
....
.... □□

48 Do you think it is possible to sum up the attitude of your non-engineering colleagues towards engineers in jobs such as yours? (*Write in fully.*)
....
....
.... □□

49 What kind of snide (*nasty*) remark do they make about the kind of work engineers do, especially in banter? (*If contact doesn't understand 'snide', say 'nasty'.*)
....
....
.... □□

50 Are you satisfied or frustrated with the status of engineers in Britain today?
....
....
.... □□

51(a) Can you say whether you personally respect more an engineering colleague who rises to the ranks of top management or one who makes a major contribution to engineering technology?

Top management 1
Technological contribution 2
Both equally 3
Other (*write in*) ....
....
....

(b) Why do you feel this way?

....
....
.... □□

52(a) Which of these professional institutions or organizations do you belong to?
(*Read out list.*)
Ask for each one mentioned:
What is your grade of membership?

If corporate member:
(b) What year did you become a corporate member of ....?

(c) What has been the extent of your activity in ....?
Would you say that you are 'very active', e.g. holding office; 'fairly active', attending meetings fairly regularly; or 'not very active'?

Organization	Corporate (*write in year*)	Non-corporate	Not a member	Very active	Fairly active	Not very active
Institution of						
Mech. Engineers	1–1	1–2	3	4	5	6
Civil Engineers	2–7	2–8	9	0	X	V
Elect. Engineers	3–1	3–2	3	4	5	6
Chemical Engineers	4–7	4–8	9	0	X	V
Marine Engineers	5–1	5–2	3	4	5	6
Water Engineers	6–7	6–8	9	0	X	V
Production Engineers	7–1	7–2	3	4	5	6
Structural Engineers	8–7	8–8	9	0	X	V
Institute of Metals	9–1	9–2	3	4	5	6
Royal Aeronautics Society	0–7	0–8	9	0	X	V
Engineers' Guild	X–1	X–2	3	4	5	6
Others (*write in*)						
	V–7	V–8	9	0	X	V

Membership

53(a) Do you think that it would be a good idea or a bad idea if all the engineering professional bodies got together to see whether they could agree to amalgamate?

Yes, good idea 1
No, bad idea 2
Don't know 3

(b) Why do you say this? (*Write in.*)

.... ☐☐

54(a) Have you published any professional articles, papers, or books?
If yes: How many?

Yes (*write in number*)
papers ....
books ....
No 3
Qualified statement (*write in*)
....
.... 4

(b) Outside of your job, have you delivered any professional papers or given any lectures? How many?

Yes (*write in number*)..............
No 7
Qualified statement (*write in*)
....
.... 8

(c) Have you made any inventions which have been patented?
If yes: How many?

Yes (*write in number*)..............
No X
Qualified statement (*write in*)
....
.... V

Now I'd like to turn briefly from your work to your leisure.

55(a) Are you a member of any non-professional organizations or clubs, such as civic, social, or political groups? (Excluding sports.)

If yes: No, none................ V
(b) Which organizations are these? (*Show card J.*)

55(c) What is the extent of your participation in ....? Would you
say you are very active, e.g. holding office; fairly active, attending meetings
fairly regularly; or not very active?

Organization	Very active	Fairly active	Not very active
Cultural groups (literary, art, theatre, etc.)	1–1	1–2	1–3
Church organizations	2–4	2–5	2–6
Ex-servicemen's groups	3–7	3–8	3–9
Trade unions	4–0	4–X	4–V
Charitable organizations	5–1	5–2	5–3
Lodges and social clubs	6–4	6–5	6–6
Political organizations	7–7	7–8	7–9
Other (*please name*)			
	8–0	8–X	8–V

56 When was the last time (apart from Christmas) you got together socially
with each of the groups of people on this card? (*Show Card K and mark all
mentioned.*)

	Within last					
	24 hrs	week	month	2–5 months	6 months or more	Never
Relatives not in household	1	2	3	4	5	6
Colleagues you work with	7	8	9	0	X	V
Other professional colleagues	1	2	3	4	5	6
Neighbours	7	8	9	0	X	V
Other friends not listed above	1	2	3	4	5	6

57 How many individuals or couples other than relatives do you consider as
close friends—even if you do not see them often?

(*Write in number*) ....

58   *If one, two, or three:*
     What is the occupation of each?
     If a couple, give husband's occupation
     only.   1 .... ☐
     If more than three: 2 .... ☐
     I'd like you to think for a minute of the 3 .... ☐
     three you know best. (*Pause*) What is the
     occupation of each? If a couple, give
     husband's occupation only.

     Ask all:
59   About how much time do you spend each week doing jobs around your
     home, on your car, or working in your garden?

                                       .... hours
                                       None V

60   Apart from this, what are your major leisure-time interests?
     How much time a month do you spend at .... ?
                                                          Time spent
                     Reading connected with work   1 .... hours
                     Other reading   2 .... hours
                     Music   3 .... hours
                     Sports   4 .... hours
                     Crafts   5 .... hours
                     Photography   6 .... hours
                     Languages   7 .... hours
                     Hobbies or interests connected
                       with work   8 .... hours
     Other interests (*write in*)

     ....
     .... 9 .... hours
                     No (other) major leisure-time interest........................... V

61(a) Have you ever travelled abroad in connexion   Yes, frequently 1
      with your work, including attendance at con-   Yes, occasionally 2
      ferences – apart from military service or jobs   No, never 3
      held abroad?

   (b) Have you a working knowledge of any foreign   French 5
       languages? If so, which?   German 6
                                                        Italian 7
                                                        Spanish 8
                                                        Russian 9
       Others (*write in*) ....
                                                        None V

62 Not counting today, about how many hours .... hours
did you spend watching TV on your own set or   Did not watch at
someone else's during the past seven days, that   all last week.......... V
is since this day last week?

63 If you had two more hours in the day – a 26-hour day – what would you
most like to do with the extra time?
If reading: Reading connected with work or not?

Relaxation, rest, sleep 1
Time with family, at home 2
Gardening, sports, other hobbies
or recreations 3
Cultural activities 4
Recreational reading 5
Work-connected reading 6
Work 7
Other (*write in*) 8
Don't know X

64(a) Which, if any, daily morning
newspapers did you read yes-
terday?
(*If Monday interview, ask about
Saturday.*)

Daily Herald 1
Daily Express 2
Daily Mail 3
Daily Mirror 4
Daily Telegraph 5
Daily Sketch 6
The Times 7
The Guardian 8
The Financial Times 9
Other (*write in*) ....
.... X
None V

(b) Which, if any, national Sunday
newspapers did you read in the
past seven days?

Sunday Express 1
Sunday Pictorial 2
Sunday Telegraph 3
Sunday Times 4
People 5
News of the World 6
Observer 7
Reynolds News 8
Other (*write in*) ....
.... X
None V

(c) Which of these weeklies/magazines do you read regularly – that is to say every issue or almost every issue? (*Show card L.*)

Economist 1
Spectator 2
Listener 3
New Statesman 4
Today 5
Time and Tide 6
New Scientist 7
Tribune 8
Nature 9
Other news & general mags./papers 10
Other scientific mags./papers 20
Other magazines/papers 30
None .... VO

65 How many English and foreign language technical journals do you read regularly? Which? (*List first 3.*)
Journals read:
1 ....
2 ....
3 ....

(*Write in total number read.*)
....

None read V

66 Which political party do you think is best for people like yourself?
Other (*write in*) ....

Conservative 1
Labour 2
Liberal 3
.... 4
Don't know 5

67 What is your religion?

Other (*write in*) ....

Church of England 6
Scottish Church 7
Non-conformist 8
Roman Catholic 9
Jewish 0
.... X
None (*skip to Q. 69*) V

68(a) About how often do you manage to attend religious services?

Never 1
Several times a year or less, e.g.
   Xmas, Easter 2
Monthly 3
Fortnightly 4
Weekly or more often 5

68(b) Where on this scale would you rate the importance or unimportance of religion in your life? (*Show Stapel scale card*)

+ □ 1
□ 2
□ 3
□ 4
□ 5
? 6
■ 7
■ 8
■ 9
■ 0
■ X
− ■ V

Ask all:

69(a) What is your present accommodation?

Rooms 1
Non self-contained flat 2
Self-contained flat 3
Entire house 4
Other (*write in*) ....
.... 5

(b) Is it fully owned by you or your family, being bought on a mortgage, rented from a private landlord, or rented from the local council?

Fully owned by you or your family 1
Being bought on a mortgage 2
Rented from a private landlord 3-6
Rented from the local council 4-6
Other (*write in*) ....
.... 5

(c) *If accommodation rented:* Is it furnished or unfurnished?

Fully furnished 6-0
Partly furnished 6-X
Unfurnished 6-V

70 If you had to say which social class you belong to, what would you say? (*Show card M.*)

Upper... 6
Upper-middle 7
Middle 8
Lower-middle 9
Working 0
Don't know X
Qualified (*write in*)
....
....

Now just a few questions about your background.

71   What year were you born?   ....

72   Where were you born? (*Parents'*   Town ....
      residence, not hospital)   County ....
                                    Abroad X

73   Have you ever been married?   Ever married 1
                                     Never married 2

      If ever married: (others skip to Q. 78)
74   What year were you first married? ....

75   How many live-born children have you had altogether?
      0   1   2   3   4   5   More than 5 ....
                                       (*write in number*)

76   *Ask all who have had any children: (others skip to Q. 78)*
      Please tell me the ages of your children and whether they are sons or
      daughters.
      If more than one: Please start with the eldest.
      If any children have died note it.

	Eldest	2	3	4	5	6	7	8	9	10
Age last birthday (*write in*)										
Boy	X	X	X	X	X	X	X	X	X	X
Girl	V	V	V	V	V	V	V	V	V	V

77(a) *Ask for each child aged five or over (starting with the eldest):*
What type of school (is he attending) (did he attend last)?

(b) *Ask for each child aged 14 or over:*
(Will he) (do you hope he will) (has he) attended university? Which one?

	Eldest	2nd	3rd	4th	5th
For each child aged five or over:					
Type of school attended now (or last attended if left school)					
Primary, elementary	1	1	1	1	1
Secondary modern/Junior secondary	2	2	2	2	2
Grammar school/Senior secondary	3	3	3	3	3
Comprehensive	4	4	4	4	4
Secondary, Technical, Commercial	5	5	5	5	5
Public or Independent day	6	6	6	6	6
Public or Independent boarding	7	7	7	7	7
Other (*write in*					
	8	8	8	8	8
For each child aged 14 or over:					
University attended or to be attended					
Oxford	1	1	1	1	1
Cambridge	2	2	2	2	2
London	3	3	3	3	3
Other (*write in*)					
	4	4	4	4	4
No university	V	V	V	V	V

If child 14 or over ask:
What occupation (is (s)he planning to take up) (has (s)he taken up)?
If under 14:
What occupation do you hope (s)he will take up?

Eldest child ....
2nd child ....
3rd child ....
4th child ....
5th child ....

Ask all:

78(a) What was the highest level of education your father completed? (*Indicate any certificates, diplomas, or degrees held.*)
If don't know: At what age did he leave school?

(b) And what about your mother?

Level of schooling	Father	Mother
Elementary only	1	1
Secondary	2	2
Technical	3	3
University	4	4
Age		
Certificates		
School exam	6	6
Technical exam	7	7
University degree	8	8
Other	9	9

79 Which of these have you in your home at the moment?

Radio	1	Electric vacuum cleaner	6
Radiogram	2	Dish-washing machine	7
Record player or gramophone	3	TV set	8
Electric washing machine	4	Car	9
Refrigerator	5	None	V

Class
AV+ 1
AV 2
AV− 3
Group D 4

Time completed .... a.m. / p.m.

Total duration of interview .... hrs. .... mins.

I hereby attest that this is an interview strictly in accordance with your directions:

Signed: ....

Date: ....

This form is the property of:

SOCIAL SURVEYS (GALLUP POLL) LTD,
211, Regent Street,
London, W.1.

o

Method of selecting the sample

Basic membership figures of the Institution of Mechanical Engineers, and sample counts from pages of the membership list for 1961, enabled estimates to be made on which to base selection from the membership list:

	No.	% total to be sampled
CORPORATE MEMBERS		
Members	4,903	10
Associate members	24,784	53
Total[a]	29,687	63
NON-CORPORATE MEMBERS		
Graduate members	17,212	37
Other non-corporate	6,844	
Total	24,056	

[a] Total comprises corporate members plus graduate members of two years' standing.

From a sample count of portions of the membership list, 13 per cent of both corporate and non-corporate members were found to have addresses abroad. Accordingly, the following approximate sampling figures were established (round numbers taken):

SELECTION OF NON-CORPORATE SAMPLE

Total of non-corporate members listed	24,000
Expectation of acceptable names (deducting 13 per cent abroad and 32 per cent of the remaining 87 per cent who were not graduate members)	59 in 100 or 14,160 in 24,000
Approximate number required (exact number of recent graduate members ineligible not known)	350
Sampling interval	40·4

Since a sample count of the number of names appearing on each page ranged from 36–42, the first name on each page was selected provided it fulfilled the sample requirements, i.e. the individual did not live abroad and he had not become a graduate member after 1959.

In order to augment the sample of university graduates the second name from the middle of each page was selected where it fulfilled the threefold requirements of residence, year of membership, and university degree. An immobile frame cut-out to expose the middle name was used for this purpose.

SELECTION OF CORPORATE MEMBERS

Selection was made irrespective of type of corporate membership. Estimates based on the membership figures produced a sampling interval similar to that for the non-corporate members; selection was therefore carried out on the same lines:

Total of corporate members listed	29,700
Expectation of acceptable names	87 in 100
(deducting 13 per cent abroad)	or 25,800 in 29,700
Approximate number required	650
Sampling interval	39·6

The sample of university graduates among the corporate members was augmented in the same way as that among the non-corporate members.

ADDITIONAL SAMPLE

When it was found that the number of successful interviews was proving lower than had been anticipated, a second sample of names was selected in order to bring the final number of successful interviews to around the desired 1,000. At this date the overall success-rate on the original sample was 61 per cent. Success-rates for the different groups (at 16 April 1962) are shown below:

	Success-rate on live names
	%
CORPORATE MEMBERS	
University graduates	65
Other	55
Total corporate	59
NON-CORPORATE MEMBERS	
University graduates	76
Other	61
Total non-corporate	65

Given the success-rate at this stage, it was necessary to select approximately a further 300 names. A variable sampling fraction was used over the different groups to take account of the considerable variations in the rate between groups. In other respects the process of selection of the additional sample followed that for the original sample. The final response-rate over the total sample is presented in Appendix 3.

Response-rate: total sample

| | Total sample | | | Type of membership[b] | | | | | |
				Corporate			Non-corporate		
	No.	%	%	No.	%.	%	No.	%	%
Total names on original list	1,499	100		1,079	100		420	100	
Less:									
Retired	100	7		100			–		
Abroad permanently or for prolonged period	54	3		38			16		
Not known, unable to trace	44[a]	3		21			23		
Dead	26	2		26			–		
Total deductions	224	15		185	17		39	9	
'Live' register	1,275	85	100	894	83	100	381	91	100
Successful interviews	977	65	77	656	61	73	321	77	84
Failures:									
Partially completed interviews	5	‡	‡	5	‡		–		
Too busy; no time for long interviews	119	8	9	98	11		21		5
Not interested in this survey; unwilling to cooperate	68	5	5	59	7		9		2
Disagree with, disapprove of, surveys in general	21	1	2	18	2		3		1
Questions too personal	3	‡	‡	1	‡		2		1
Out at 3 or more calls; failed to keep appointment	52	3	4	34	4		18		5
Had to refuse for security reasons	8	1	1	7	1		1		‡
Retired as engineer and declined interview	2	‡	‡	2	‡		–		
Contact ill; member of family ill; too worried; couldn't spare time	20	1	1	14	2		6		2
Total failures	298	20	23	238	22	27	60	14	16

[a] Of these 44, 8 had lapsed membership of the Institution of Mechanical Engineers.

[b] Between the time of the compilation of the membership list from which the sample was drawn an completion of fieldwork, some of the contacts had become corporate members. In drawing the sampl graduate status could be ascribed only to those members showing appropriate letters after their name At the interviews, it was found that some additional respondents were graduates or had obtained a degre since the compliation of the list.

University status						Type of membership × University status											
						Corporate						Non-corporate					
Graduate			Non-graduate			Graduate			Non-graduate			Graduate			Non-graduate		
No.	%	%	No.	%	%	No.	%	%	No.	%	%	No.	%	%	No.	%	%
501	100		998	100		382	100		697	100		119	100		301	100	
28			72			28			72			–			–		
16			38			13			25			3			13		
14			30			7			14			7			16		
6			20			6			20			–			–		
64	13		160	16		54	14		131	19		10	8		29	10	
437	87	100	838	84	100	328	86	100	566	81	100	109	92	100	272	90	100
358	71	82	619	62	74	263	69	80	393	56	70	95	80	87	226	72	83
–			5		1	–			5		1	–			–		
31		7	88		10	27		8	71		12	4		4	17		6
21		5	47		6	20		6	39		7	1		1	8		3
5		1	16		2	5		2	13		2	–			3		1
–			3		#	–			1		#				2		1
16		4	36		4	9		3	25		4	7		6	11		4
1		#	7		1	1		#	6		1	–			1		#
–			2		#	–			2		#	–			–		
5		1	15		2	3		1	11		2	2		2	4		1
79	16	18	219	22	26	65	17	20	173	25	30	14	12	13	46	18	17

•

Recent developments affecting status and training

Since the first draft of this book was written several things have happened which may have an important influence upon the development of the engineering profession in Britain. It is therefore necessary to provide a brief review of these events in order to complete the picture and bring the reader up to date with the situation.

On 3 August 1965 the Queen granted a Royal Charter to the Council of the Engineering Institutions (CEI), which in its formative stage had been known as the Engineering Institutions Joint Council (EIJC).[1] Professional engineers who were on that date corporate members of the thirteen institutions listed on page 10 are now entitled to describe themselves as Chartered Engineers and to use the abbreviation C.Eng. To become a Chartered Engineer after 1970 one must have passed the CEI examinations or have obtained exemption by having a degree. There has thus been a considerable increase in the minimum educational standard required, and the Parts 1 and 2 examinations are together comparable in attainment to a university pass degree. Part 1, representing the first half of a nine-term degree course, is a common examination for all institutions, and Part 2 will allow a choice of subjects depending on the field of engineering in which candidates are employed. The possibility of further requirements or a Part 3 examination is being considered by some institutions. The CEI and its qualifying regulations are likely to have an important effect upon the pattern of recruitment and it is probable that in future most engineers will qualify via a university degree course or a Council for National Academic Awards degree course at a recognized Technical College.

The first steps therefore towards the unification of the diverse engineering profession have been taken, but it is important to note that the function of CEI is largely that of a learned society and that

[1] For references, see end of this appendix.

the wider professional functions covered by the Engineers' Guild have not been incorporated. For instance, Section 3 of the Charter states:

'The object for which the Council is hereby constituted is to promote and co-ordinate in the public interest the development of the science, art and practice of engineering and for that purpose:

(i) to establish, uphold and advance the standards of qualification, competence and conduct of professional engineers;

(ii) to advance the aims and objectives of its Members, so far as they relate to the advancement of the science, art or practice of engineering;

(iii) to foster relations with the Government, with national and international bodies at all levels of technical and professional competence, whose objects and purposes may be related to those of the Council;

(iv) to foster co-operation with Universities and other educational institutions:

(v) to foster co-operation between its Members on matters pertaining to the science, art or practice of engineering;

(vi) to acquire by purchase, devise, bequest, donation or otherwise lands and hereditaments of any description and tenure and to accept any gift, endowment or bequest and the office of trustee and to carry out any trust attached to any such gift, endowment or bequest or attached to such office;

(vii) to do all such lawful things as are incidental or conducive to the attainment of that object' (Ref. 1).

The Engineers' Guild and the CEI have not found it possible to merge at this stage and have therefore agreed to continue their separate activities. The following statement to clarify the situation has been adopted by the Board of CEI.

'*Background*

The Guild was brought into existence in 1938 by the individual efforts of some members of the Institutions of Civil, Mechanical and Electrical Engineers. After a period of relative quiescence during the War its membership passed the thousand mark in 1948, and is now about six thousand. It has, throughout its existence, been supported by the direct subscriptions of its members, a separate entity from the Institutions and prohibited from such actions as would make it a trade union. Until 1957, membership was limited to members of the three above-mentioned Institutions. It is now open to all members of the Institutions who are constituents of the Council.

In the Memorandum of Association of the Guild, three of the objects are relevant to this paper. The first, a general one, is to promote and maintain the unity, public usefulness, honour and interests of the engineering profession.

The second deals with Parliamentary or similar action on matters affecting the interests of the engineering profession. The third is concerned with legal action to further the interests of the profession or to protect the rights and interests of individual members.

The setting-up of the Engineering Institutions Joint Council in 1962 as a federated body, maintained by grants from the thirteen Chartered Institutions, foreshadowed a significant change in the position of the Guild which previously had been the only co-operative body of professional engineers, apart from the Institutions themselves. The primary object of the Council as stated in the Royal Charter granted in 1965, is "to establish, uphold and advance the standard of qualification, competence and conduct of professional engineers" which includes some generalities similar to the first object of the Guild but the interpretation of which is dependent on the other objects for which the Council was formed. The second and third objects of the Council are more significant and are:

"To advance the aims and objects of its members (Institutions) so far as they relate to the advancement of the science, art or practice of engineering.

To foster relations with Government, with national and international bodies and with the public; and to co-operate with other bodies at all levels of technical and professional competence whose objects may be related to the Council."

Thus whilst the Council is concerned with the structure of the profession and the needs of its member Institutions in so far as they relate to the advancement of the profession, it is not concerned with services to individual engineers, such services having been, through the years, the responsibility of the Guild. Even though the main division of interest between the two bodies is apparent, there is much that is ill-defined. Engineering and engineers cannot always be dealt with in isolation from each other and the Council's work, at times, will inevitably be concerned with general matters of professional interest.

A joint EIJC/Guild Committee was set up in 1962, the first term of reference of which was to examine the respective aims and functions; the second to consider how best the two bodies could co-operate in the future. The Committee has achieved some co-ordination of effort but made little progress towards developing a pattern of co-operation for the future. Reasons for this have been the fact that the Council has not so far determined its own policy and that the Guild has been concerned with the possible impact on its viability of the Council's activities. Because of these differences there is every reason for the joint Committee to continue its efforts at co-ordination, in the interests of the profession as a whole.

Policy

1. The Council's relationship with the Guild must take into account the charitable status of the Constituent Institutions of the Council and that the Council itself has applied for charitable status.
2. The Guild's work of covering personal services in relation to salaries, pensions, legal problems, service agreements and appointments, lies outside the field of work of the Council and will continue to do so.
3. With the size of task that lies ahead there is abundant work for both the Council and the Guild. The division of effort and relative responsibilities must be settled with due regard to terms of reference, respective resources and views on relative priorities.
4. The Joint CEI/Guild Committee should continue as a means of exchanging information on each other's work and developing co-operation in the interests of the profession as a whole' (Ref. 2).

It is quite clear, therefore, that the engineering profession in Britain still has no single authoritative body to represent its views on all professional and technical matters, but at least a start has been made to unify the learned society activities and to maintain entry standards which are more comparable with those in other European countries. Some day, perhaps, CEI and Engineers' Guild will unite to form a powerful body that can speak with authority on all aspects of the engineering profession.

Another important event has been the decision by the Government, in line with the recommendations of the Robbins Report, to make the ten Colleges of Advanced Technology into independent degree-giving universities. The only exceptions so far are that the Chelsea CAT is to become a college of London University rather than a completely separate institution, and that negotiations are in progress for the Welsh CAT to become a constituent college of the University of Wales. The establishment of these new technological universities in some ways confuses the educational picture because, apart from the sandwich nature of the CAT degree courses, there is not much difference between their content and that of many applied science degrees at the universities. Somewhere in the development process the original objective of the CATs to produce technologists has been lost.

Another complicating factor is the Labour government's policy on higher education and their so-called binary system, whereby large numbers of young people will be encouraged to take degree-level courses at recognized technical colleges. This has been described in a recent White Paper (Ref. 3) which outlines proposals to make many of the regional technical colleges into 'Polytechnics' where it will be possible to take all kinds of part-time and full-time courses. As far as degree-level courses are concerned, it will be interesting to see whether the Polytechnics will succeed in producing technologists or whether once again they will be tempted to copy the universities and thereby add to the general confusion in higher education. It is obviously important to avoid duplication and wastage of teaching staff and expensive buildings and laboratories, and it remains to be seen whether the new educational programme will be economical or not. Whatever the results, it is likely that a much higher proportion of professional engineers will qualify by full-time courses.

As a result of the greatly improved opportunities for full-time education, there may be a shortage of technical supporting staff for engineers because able people on the shop-floor will be encouraged to go up through the higher educational system and possibly qualify as chartered engineers. We have already noted the beginning of this trend in the engineering profession, and it is now likely to increase. The correct distribution of technical and scientific manpower is therefore of great national importance and deserves very careful consideration. A start in this direction was made on 4 February 1965, when the government set up a Committee on Manpower Resources for Science and Technology under the chairmanship of Sir Willis

Jackson to study such problems. This committee and its various working groups have produced several valuable publications about the technical manpower issue (Ref. 4). Much useful information has been obtained and recommendations have been made for the future collection of more systematic data on all levels of technical activity. For instance, some of their publications have covered the topics mentioned in the next paragraph.

In addition to outlining the problem and the work of the Scientific and Technical Manpower Committee, Ref. 1 refers to the other committee under Sir Willis Jackson's chairmanship which is making a joint inquiry on technicians. Preliminary results show that about two-thirds of the so-called technicians have no recognized qualifications. The flow of school-leavers into various disciplines is analysed in the Dainton Report (Ref. 5), from which it appears that there has been a very rapid increase in the proportion taking economics, politics, and social science subjects. Ref. 6 reviews the first employment of graduates and reveals the very different patterns among scientists and engineers, a much higher proportion of the latter going into industry. The Arthur Report (Ref. 7) analyses the limitations of present post-graduate courses and emphasizes the need for closer collaboration in future between industry and the universities. In Ref. 8 the Bosworth Committee makes some original proposals for a carefully designed matching section to provide the graduate trainee with the necessary industrial and professional background that will best fit him for early responsibility in industry. The Industrial Training Act (1964) and its compulsory levy may give valuable backing not only to the training of technicians but also to the induction of young professional engineers. Ref. 9 provides a valuable analysis of the factors influencing scientists and engineers in their choice of jobs.

From all these activities it is clear that an attempt is being made in Britain to keep reliable stock records of her manpower and to try to distribute it to the best advantage. As part of this process the importance of engineers to the national economy is becoming more obvious.

REFERENCES

1. *The Chartered Mech. Engr.* October 1965, 543.
2. *Prof. Engr.* **2**, 1966, 90.

3. *A plan for polytechnics and other colleges.* Cmd. 3006. London: HMSO, May 1966.
4. *A review of the scope and problems of scientific and technical man-power policy.* Cmd. 2800. London: HMSO, October 1965.
5. *Enquiry into the flow of candidates in science and technology into higher education – interim report.* Cmd. 2893. London: HMSO, Feb. 1966.
6. *First employment of university graduates, 1963–64.* London: HMSO, 1965.
7. *Enquiry into longer-term postgraduate courses for engineers and technologists, 1964–65.* London: HMSO, 1965.
8. *Education and training requirements for the electrical and mechanical manufacturing industries.* London: HMSO, 1966.
9. *Scientists and engineers and their choice of jobs, 1956–59.* Department of Education and Science. London: HMSO, 1966.

References

ABRAMS, Mark (1964). *Architects.* A survey conducted for *The Observer.* London: Research Services Ltd.

ABRAMS, Mark & ROSE, Richard (1960). *Must Labour lose?* Harmondsworth, Middx: Penguin Books.

ACTON SOCIETY TRUST (1956). *Management succession.* London: The Acton Society Trust.

ADVISORY COUNCIL ON SCIENTIFIC POLICY, Committee on Scientific Manpower, 1962 (1963). *Scientific and technological manpower in Great Britain.* Cmnd. 2146. London: HMSO.

AITCHISON, J. & BROWN, J. A. C. (1957). *The lognormal distribution.* London: Cambridge University Press.

ASHBY, Eric (1958). *Technology and the academics.* London: Macmillan; New York: St Martin's Press.

AXELROD, Morris (1956). Urban structure and social participation. *Amer. sociol. Rev.* 21, 13–18.

BARBER, Bernard (1952). *Science and the social order.* Glencoe, Ill.: Free Press.

BARBER, Bernard (1963). Some problems in the sociology of the professions. *Daedalus* 92, 669–88.

BARBER, Bernard & HIRSCH, Walter (1962). *The sociology of science.* New York: Free Press.

BECKER, Howard S., *et al.* (1961). *Boys in white.* Chicago: University of Chicago Press.

BECKER, Howard S. & CARPER, James (1956). The elements of identification with an occupation. *Amer. sociol. Rev.* 21, 341–8.

BLAUNER, Robert (1960). Work stratification and industrial trends in modern society. In W. Galenson & S. M. Lipset (Eds.), *Labor and trade unionism.* New York: Wiley.

BLONDEL, J. (1963). *Voters, parties and leaders; the social fabric of British politics.* Harmondsworth, Middx.: Penguin Books.

BOWDEN, B. V. (1959). Case for university reform. *The Guardian,* 8 December.

THE BRITISH ASSOCIATION (1961). *The complete scientist.* London: Oxford University Press.

BUCHER, Rue & STRAUSS, Anselm (1961). Professions in process. *Amer. J. Sociol.* 66, 325–34.

CAPLOW, Theodore & MCGEE, Reece (1958). *The academic marketplace.* New York: Basic Books.

CARR-SAUNDERS, A. M. (1958). *A social survey of social conditions in England and Wales.* Oxford: Clarendon Press.

CARR-SAUNDERS, A. M. & WILSON, P. A. (1933). *The professions.* Oxford: Clarendon Press.

CARTER, C. E. (1963). *The distribution of scientific effort.* London: Minerva.

214

References ·215

CAUTER, T. & DOWNHAM, J. S. (1954). *The communication of ideas*. London: Chatto & Windus.

The Chartered Mechanical Engineer (1963). The professions in our national life. June, p. 307.

CLARKE, Alfred C. (1956). Leisure and occupational prestige. *Amer. sociol. Rev.* 21, 301–7.

CLEMENTS, R. V. (1958). *Managers: a study of their careers in industry*. London: Allen & Unwin.

COPEMAN, G. H. (1955). *Leaders of British industry*. London: Gee.

CRAIG, Christine (1963). *The employment of Cambridge graduates*. London: Cambridge University Press.

DEDIJER, Stevan (1962). Measuring the growth of science. *Science* 138, 781–87.

DEPARTMENT OF SCIENTIFIC & INDUSTRIAL RESEARCH (1963). *Engineering design*. Report of a committee appointed by the Council for Scientific and Industrial Research to consider the present standing of mechanical engineering design. (Chairman: G. B. R. Feilden.) London: HMSO.

DOUGLAS, J. W. B. (1964). *The home and the school*. London: MacGibbon & Kee.

The Economist (1964). Salaries: are you better off? 23 May, pp. 813–15; 30 May, pp. 926–9.

EDINBURGH, DUKE OF (1961). The engineer in commonwealth development. (Seventh Graham Clark lecture.) *Proc. Instn. Civil Engrs.*, London.

ENGINEERS' GUILD (1961). Professional engineers' income 1959–60. *Prof. Engr.* 6, 329–49.

ENGINEERS' GUILD (1963). A parliament for engineers (FEANI). *Prof. Engr.* 8, 5, 159–60.

ENGINEERS' GUILD (1964a). The Guild and the EI(J)C. *Prof. Engr.* 9, 3, 85–7.

ENGINEERS' GUILD (1964b). *Professional engineers' incomes 1962–63*. London: The Engineers' Guild Ltd.

EUSEC (1961). (The conference of engineering societies of Western Europe and the USA) *Report on education and training of professional engineers*. Brussels: Robert Louis.

The Financial Times (1963). How salaries in the professions compare. 18 December, p. 13.

FOGARTY, Michael (1964). *The rules of work*. London: Geoffrey Chapman.

GERSTL, Joel E. (1961a). Determinants of occupational community in high status occupations. *Sociol. Quart.* 2, 37–48.

GERSTL, Joel E. (1961b). Leisure, taste and occupational milieu. *Soc. Problems* 9, 56–68.

GERSTL, Joel E. & COHEN, Lois K. (1964). Dissensus, situs and egocentrism in occupational ranking. *Brit. J. Sociol.* 15, 254–61.

GERSTL, Joel E. & PERRUCCI, Robert (1965). Comparative social mobility: one occupation in two societies. *Sociol. Educ.* 38, 224–32.

GINZBERG, Eli, *et al.* (1951). *Occupational choice; an approach to a general theory*. New York: Columbia University Press.

GLASER, Barney G. (1964). *Organizational scientists: their professional careers*. Indianapolis: Bobbs-Merrill.

P

216 · Engineers: the anatomy of a profession

GOODE, William J. (1960). Encroachment, charlatanism, and the emerging profession. *Amer. sociol. Rev.* **25**, 902–14.

GOULDNER, Alvin W. (1957–58). Cosmopolitans and locals: toward an analysis of latent social roles. *Admin. Sci. Quart.* **2**, 281–306 and 444–80.

GRINTER, L., *et al.* (1955). Final report on evaluation of engineering education. *J. engng. Educ.* **46**, 26–60.

HABENSTEIN, Robert W. (1963). Critique of 'profession' as a sociological category. *Sociol. Quart.* **4**, 291–300.

HARTLEY, Sir Harold (1964). The contribution of engineering to the British economy. *The Chartered mech. Engr.*, June, pp. 312–17.

HAVEMANN, Ernest & WEST, Patricia (1952). *They went to college.* New York: Harcourt Brace.

HAVIGHURST, Robert J. & FEIGENBAUM, Kenneth (1959). Leisure and life style. *Amer. J. Sociol.* **64**, 396–404.

HAWKINS, G. A., THOMA, E. C. & LEBOLD, W. K. (1959). A study of the Purdue University engineering graduate. *J. engng. Educ.* **49**, 930–47.

HODGES, Harold M., Jr. (1964). *Social stratification – class in America.* Cambridge, Mass.: Schenkman.

HUGHES, Everett C. (1958). *Men and their work.* Glencoe, Ill.: Free Press.

HUTCHINGS, D. W. (1963). *Technology and the sixth form boy.* Oxford: Univ. Dept. of Education.

HUTTON, S. P. (1962). *Evolution and engineering.* Cardiff: University of Wales Press.

HUTTON, S. P. & GERSTL, J. E. (1963). Career patterns of mechanical engineers. *Prof. Engr.* **8**, 85–9.

INSTITUTION OF CHEMICAL ENGINEERS (1964). *The choice of chemical engineering at university or technical college.* London: Instn. Chem. Engrs.

JACKSON, B. & MARSDEN, D. (1962). *Education and the working class.* London: Routledge & Kegan Paul.

JENKINS, Hester & JONES, D. C. (1950). Social class of Cambridge alumni. *Brit. J. Sociol.* **1**, 93–116.

JOHNSTONE, R. E. (1961). A survey of chemical engineering education and practice. *Trans. Instn. chem. Engrs.*, London.

JONES, Gareth (1963). The distribution of talent between science and technology. *New Scientist* **324** (31 Jan.), 239–40.

KELSALL, Roger Keith (1955). *Higher civil servants in Britain, from 1870 to the present day.* London: Routledge & Kegan Paul.

KORNHAUSER, William (1962). *Scientist in industry: conflict and accommodation.* London: Cambridge University Press; Berkeley & Los Angeles: University of California Press.

KUBIE, Lawrence S. (1954). Some unsolved problems of the scientific career. *Amer. Scientist* **42**, 104–12. Reprinted in B. Barber & W. Hirsch (Eds.), *The sociology of science.* New York: Free Press, 1962.

LARRABEE, Eric (1958). What's happening to hobbies? In Eric Larrabee & Rolf Meyersohn (Eds.), *Mass leisure.* Glencoe, Ill.: Free Press.

LEBOLD, William K., *et al.* (1960). A study of the Purdue University engineering graduate. Lafayette, Ind.: *Purdue Engineering Bulletin 64.*

LEWIS, R. & MAUDE, A. (1952). *Professional people.* London: Phoenix House.

LIPSET, Seymour Martin (1960). *Political man.* New York: Doubleday.

The Listener (1962). 19 April, p. 710; 19 July, p. 119.

LOVE, P. P. (1956). A criticism of the technical education of recently qualified engineers. *Proc. Instn. mech. Engrs.* **170**, 3, 127–56. London.

LYNES, Russell (1955). *The tastemakers.* New York: Harper.

MACFARLANE, Bruce A. (1961). The chartered engineer: a study of the recruitment, qualifications, conditions of employment, and professional associations of chartered civil, electrical and mechanical engineers in Great Britain. Ph.D. (London) thesis, unpublished.

MARCSON, Simon (1960). *The scientist in American industry.* Princeton: Industrial Relations Section, Princeton University.

MEAD, Margaret & METRAUX, Rhoda (1957). The image of the scientist among high school students. *Science* **126**, 384–90. Reprinted in B. Barber & W. Hirsch (Eds.), *The sociology of science.* New York: Free Press, 1962.

MERTON, Robert K., *et al.* (1957). *The student-physician.* Cambridge: Harvard University Press.

MILLERSON, Geoffrey (1964). *The qualifying associations: a study in professionalisation.* London: Routledge & Kegan Paul.

MINISTRY OF EDUCATION (1963a). *Higher education.* Report of the Committee on Higher Education (Chairman: Lord Robbins) 1961–63 (Cmnd. 2154). London: HMSO.

MINISTRY OF EDUCATION (1963b). *Half our future.* A report of the Central Advisory Council for Education (England). (Chairman: J. H. Newsom.) London: HMSO.

MORSE, Nancy C. & WEISS, Robert S. (1955). The function and meaning of work and the job. *Amer. sociol. Rev.* **20**, 191–8.

New Society (1963a). The empty title. No. 44, 1 August, p. 5.

New Society (1963b). Manpower – a pipe dream? No. 56, 24 October, pp. 21–2.

New Society (1964). Careers: shifting patterns. No. 98, 13 August, p. 22

OPINION RESEARCH CORP. (1959). *The conflict between the scientific mind and the management mind.* Princeton, N.J.: ORC.

PARSONS, Talcott (1939). The professions and social structure. *Soc. Forces* **17**, 457–67. Reprinted in *Essays in sociological theory.* Glencoe, Ill.: Free Press, 1954.

PELZ, Donald C. (1956). Some social factors related to performance in a research organization. *Admin. Sci. Quart.* **1**, 310–25.

PEP (Political and Economic Planning) (1957). *Graduates in industry.* London: Allen & Unwin.

PERRUCCI, Robert (1961). The significance of intra-occupational mobility. *Amer. sociol. Rev.* **26**, 874–83.

PIERCE, Rachel M. (1964). Special tabulations provided by the author, derived from Rachel M. Pierce & Griselda Rowntree (1961), Birth control in Britain. *Population Studies* **15**, 121–48.

RAPOPORT, Robert N. (1964). The male's occupation in relation to his decision to marry. *Acta Sociologica* **8**, 68–82.

REISSMAN, Leonard (1949). A study of role conceptions in bureaucracy. *Soc. Forces* **27**, 305–10.

RIESMAN, David & ROSENBOROUGH, Howard (1955). *Careers and consumer behavior. Consumer behavior*, Vol. 2. New York: New York University.

RILLIE, John A. M. (1964). The sweet smell of failure. *The twentieth Century* **172**, 85–99.

SOCIAL SURVEYS (GALLUP POLL) (1963). *Technical staff recruitment survey.* London.

STRAUSS, Anselm L. & RAINWATER, Lee (1962). *The professional scientist – a study of American chemists.* Chicago: Aldine.

TIMOSHENKO, S. (1959). *Engineering education in Russia.* New York: McGraw-Hill.

US DEPARTMENT OF COMMERCE (1963). *Studies in scientific and engineering manpower.* (Staff Report: 63–1.) Washington: GPO.

US PRESIDENT'S COMMITTEE ON ENGINEERS AND SCIENTISTS FOR FEDERAL GOVERNMENT PROGRAMS (1957). *Summary report of survey of attitudes of scientists and engineers in government and industry.* Washington: GPO.

VEBLEN, Thorstein (1921). *The engineers and the price system.* New York: B. W. Huebsch.

WHYTE, William H., Jr. (1956). *The organization man.* New York: Simon & Schuster; London: Cape, 1957.

WILENSKY, Harold L. (1956). *Intellectuals in labor unions.* Glencoe, Ill.: Free Press.

WILENSKY, Harold L. (1961). The uneven distribution of leisure. *Soc. Problems* **9**, 32–56.

WILENSKY, Harold L. (1964a). The professionalization of everyone? *Amer. J. sociol.* **70**, 137–58.

WILENSKY, Harold L. (1964b). Varieties of work experience. In Henry Borow (Ed.), *Man in a world of work.* Boston: Houghton Mifflin.

WILLMOTT, Peter & YOUNG, Michael (1960). *Family and class in a London suburb.* London: Routledge & Kegan Paul.

WOODWARD, Joan (1958). *Management and technology.* DSIR, Problems of Progress in Industry, No. 2. London: HMSO.

YOUNG, Michael & WILLMOTT, Peter (1957). *Family and kinship in East London.* London: Routledge & Kegan Paul.

Subject index

A-level examination, taken by engineers, 32
academic standards, maintenance of, 168-9
administrative orientation, of engineers, 121-3
aero-engineering,
  employment of engineers trained in, 61-2
age, of engineers,
  and administrative orientation, 122-123
  and attitude to non-attendance at university, 53, 54
  and career goals, 102
  and career types, 90
  and commitment, 126-7
  and dissatisfaction, 121
  and hobbies, 139
  and leisure patterns, 144, 152
  and mobility, 94-9
  and professional ambience, 133-4
  and professional productivity, 132
  and social relations, 140
  and subjects studied, 61
    non-technical, 59
  and subordinates, 79
  and university attendance, 46
  as variable, 20, 155
apprenticeships,
  length of, 66
  and university graduates, 43, 66
armed forces, engineers employed in, 69, 91
aspirations, of engineers,
  and expectations, 106
  for children, 110-12
  and income, 107-8
  and work orientation, 122
attainment, see 'success'
Australia, university population in, 12

authority, of engineer, 77-8
automatic control, 58, 60
autonomy, of engineers, definition of, 18

birth, place of, of engineers, 30, 86-7
'brain drain', 49
Bosworth Committee, 212
Britain,
  diversification of engineering profession in, 11
  engineering education in, 7-8, 12-13, 39-67, 167-71
  engineering institutions in, 9-10
  status of engineer in, 12-13, 165-6
  university population in, 12
  vagueness of term 'engineer' in, 5
British Institute of Radio Engineers, 10
British Medical Association, 153
  and Engineers' Guild, 10

Camford (university category),
  curricula at, 57-9
  degrees awarded by, 47-8
  engineers attending, 45-6
    children of, 111
    schools attended by, 48
    and success, 51
  higher degrees at, 49
career choices, of engineers, alternative, 127-8
career goals, of engineers, 102
career orientation, of engineers,
  and aspirations, 122
  and career type, 92, 123
  as dependent variable, 20
  dichotomy in, 121-2
  and organizational demands, 123
  of part-time students, 43
  and professional productivity, 132-3

219

engineers—*contd.*
efficient use of, 11, 161–2, 168
recommendations on, 171–2
evolution of, 1–2
expectations of, 106–8
and foreign languages, 76–7
friendship patterns of, 133–4
hobbies of, 138–9
home life of, 136–7
income of, 18, 103–6
and success, 20, 28
manual work by, 76
marriage patterns of, 28–9, 135–6
mobility of employment of, 94–9, 109–10
newspapers read by, 146–9
occupational choice by, 35–8
occupational hierarchy, place of in, 114–17
occupational inheritance among, 111
off duty, 19, 135–52
and place of birth, 86–7
political attitudes of, 145–6
and professional associations, 128–130
professional, definition of, 4–5, 7–8, 9–11, 35
professional productivity of, 131–3
qualifications of, 18
recommendations concerning, 162–172
recruitment of, 19, 24–38, 163–4
social basis of, 24–30
and religion, 149–51
requirement of, 15, 163–65
routine work by, 75–6, 171
schools attended by, 30–5, 163
self-placement in social class by, 29–30
shortage of, 165–6
social origins of, 24–30
sociological studies of, 16–17
status of, 11–12, 19, 24, 68, 74–83, 100–17
and subordinates, 77, 78–80
title protected by law, 5
training of, 39–67
usefulness of, 59–62

travel abroad by, 76
type of work done by, 72–7
work-connected reading of, 133
work setting of, 68–83
Engineers' Guild, 8, 10–11, 130, 166
and CEI, 208–10
and EIJC, 10–11, 210
and income, 103
survey of graduates by, 56
Europe, training and grading of engineers in, 7, 8, 166
EUSEC (Conference of Engineering Societies of Western Europe and the USA)
and definition of professional engineer, 4–5, 7
expectations, of engineers,
and aspirations, 106
and income, 107–8
and mobility, 109–10
and organizational ladders, 108–9
summary of, 156
external degree, in engineering, 41
decrease in numbers taking, 44

father's profession, and success of engineers, 27–8
Fédération Européene d'Associations Nationales d'Ingénieurs (FEANI), 8, 166
Feilden Committee, 172
fluid mechanics, 58, 60
foreign languages,
in 'ideal' course, 63–4
knowledge of, 76–7
use of, 61, 62
friendship patterns, of engineers, 133–4
full-time courses, 41, 43

General Medical Council, and EIJC, 10
geographical mobility of employment, 97–8
Germany, 'engineer' a legally protected term in, 5
graduate apprenticeships, 42, 161
graduate members, definition of, 21, 39

and children's attendance at university, 111
criteria of, 20, 100
and father's status, 27-8
and first job, 85
graduates and non-graduates, 50-2, 154-5, 159-60
and home-life, 137
and industry, 70, 155
and job title, 101-2
and organizational involvement, 142
and social relations, 140
and specialization in education, 58
and status, 96-8
and subordinates, 78-80
summary, 154-5
and work-connected reading, 133
survey,
procedures employed in, 21-3
questionnaire, 173-202
recommendations from, 162-72
sample-selection technique in, 203-7
scope of, 17-20
summary of results from, 153-7

technical colleges,
attitudes of engineers to, 65
employment of engineers by, 69
technical labour, efficient use of, 11, 161
technical orientation, and administrative orientation, 121-2
technicians, 14-15
training of, 168
Technische Hochschulen, 7
technological universities, 211
technologists,
colleagues' evaluation of, 123-4
and technicians, 14
television, viewing of, by engineers, 136-7

The Complete Scientist, 63, 169
thermodynamics, 58, 60
travel, by engineers, 76
'two-tier' structure of engineering, 153-154
and institutional membership, 162

United States,
employment of engineers in, 89
leisure patterns in, 144
political attitudes of engineers in, 145
recruitment of engineers in, 27
training and status of engineers in, 8, 9, 39, 63
university,
attitudes of engineers to, 52-6, 65
categories of, 45
courses in engineering at, 41, 160-1
ideal, 62-4
non-technical subjects in, 58-9, 169
recommendations for, 169
engineers' children at, 111
engineers, employed in, 68, 69
priorities at, 164-5
reasons of engineers for non-attendance at, 53
technological, 211
type of, attended by engineers, 33, 45-6
variation in standard of degrees at, 47-8

weekly papers, read by engineers, 148-9
work setting, of engineers, 68-83
frustration in, 120-1
hours of work, 82-3
number of professional colleagues, 80-1
work study, 58, 60

Author index

228